The dignity of risk

A practical handbook for professionals working
with disabled children and their families

COUNCIL FOR
DISABLED
CHILDREN

Shared Care Network

National Children's Bureau
8 Wakley Street
London EC1V 7QE

© 2004 Council for Disabled Children
ISBN 1 904787 22 3

Disclaimer

This handbook is intended as guidance only and should not be treated as an authoritative interpretation of the law, which is a matter for the courts.

Photocopying

The materials in this handbook are designed to be shared. Forms can be photocopied and adapted for local services and settings. We would like to continue this sharing, so please, as you develop your practice further, send electronic copies to Shared Care Network and the Council for Disabled Children.

Risks

To laugh is to risk being a fool
To weep is to risk being sentimental
To reach out for another is to risk involvement
To show feelings is to risk showing yourself

To place your ideas, your dreams
Before a crowd is to risk their loss
To love is to risk not being loved in return
To live is to risk dying
To hope is to risk despair
To try is to risk failure

But risks must be taken because the greatest
Hazard in life is to risk nothing
Those who risk nothing do nothing, have nothing
And are nothing

They may avoid suffering and sorrow
But they cannot learn, feel change,
Grow, love, live

Chained by their certainties, they are slaves
They have forfeited their freedom.
Only a person who risks ... is truly free.

Anon

Shared Care Network is the national organisation representing family-based short break services for disabled children and young people in England, Wales and Northern Ireland.

Short break services provide opportunities for disabled children and other children in need, to spend time away from their primary carers. They give disabled children and young people the chance to gain independence and expand their social lives while their families get a break from caring.

Short breaks may take place in the child's own home, the home of an approved carer or in any other community setting. Short breaks can be anything from a few hours a week to a few days a month and may include an overnight stay. Short breaks can include day, evening, overnight or weekend activities. They may include services such as sitting and overnight sitting (in the child's own home), daycare and overnight stays (in the carer's own home) and befriending, as well as Saturday and after-school clubs and inclusive leisure.

Shared Care Network promotes the development of quality, short break services by running training and conferences, operating an information and advice service, producing publications and through its research programme which informs policy and practice.

Shared Care Network
63–66 Easton Business Centre
Felix Road
Easton
Bristol
BS5 0HE

tel 0117 941 5361

fax 0117 941 5362

minicom 0117 941 5364

web www.sharedcarenetwork.org.uk

email shared-care@bristol.ac.uk

The Council for Disabled Children (formerly the Voluntary Council for Handicapped Children) was established in 1974. It is an independently elected, multidisciplinary consortium operating under the aegis of the National Children's Bureau.

The Council for Disabled Children (CDC) promotes collaborative work and partnership between various agencies, parents and children, and provides a national forum for the discussion, development and dissemination of a wide range of policy and practice issues relating to service provision and support for children and young people with disabilities and special educational needs.

CDC's broad-based membership and our contacts with an extensive network of individuals and agencies, both large and small, national and local, gives us a unique overview of current issues and assists us in promoting quality services and support for children and their families.

CDC aims to:
- raise awareness of the needs of disabled children and their families
- contribute to the development of policy and practice in central and local government
- promote the participation of disabled children and their families in all decision making about their lives
- provide an independent national forum for the discussion and resolution of issues relating to children and disability.

The specific objectives of CDC include:
- identifying and disseminating information on current policy and practice, research and training
- advising and working with government and local authority departments, health authorities and NHS trusts, schools and voluntary organisations
- responding to new directions in the development of services and legislation
- advising on gaps and overlaps in service provision and encouraging inter-agency working.

Council for Disabled Children
8 Wakley Street
London EC1V 7QE

tel 020 7843 1900

fax 020 7843 6313

Contents

Acknowledgements *vi*

Foreword *vii*

1 Introduction *1*

Risk management: the context *1*
Key principles underlying the handbook *3*
How to use this handbook *4*
References *5*

2 Health and safety *6*

The definition of risk *6*
Managing risk *6*
Designing safe services *6*
Common scenarios *9*
Risk management and standards *10*
References *13*
Sample forms and guidance *13*

3 Meeting children's health care needs *23*

Intimate and personal care *23*
Invasive care *24*
Policy framework needed to ensure service provision *25*
Policy guidance: what needs to be in place? *27*
Conclusion *30*
References *30*
Checklist of key points: invasive clinical procedures *31*
Sample forms and guidance *32*

4 Moving and handling *70*

The legislative framework *70*
Survey of moving and handling issues *71*
The East Sussex judgment *72*
Policy guidance: what needs to be in place? *73*
Conclusion *75*
References *76*
Checklist of key points: moving and handling *77*
Appendix: The law in detail *78*
Sample forms and guidance *79*

5 Physical interventions for challenging behaviour/managing behaviour *97*

Policy guidance *97*
Policy for Shared Care services *98*
Managing risk and physical interventions *99*
Policy guidance: what needs to be in place? *102*
Conclusion *104*
References *104*
Checklist of key points: restrictive physical interventions *105*
Appendix: Policy guidance in detail *106*
Sample forms and guidance *108*

6 Towards child-centred risk management *119*

Communication and communication passports *119*
Final thoughts in relation to managing risk *120*
Examples of communication passports *121*

Acknowledgements

This handbook was written by Christine Lenehan, Director of the Council for Disabled Children, Jan Morrison, Principal Policy Officer for Disability at Barnardo's and freelance consultant, and Jonathan Stanley, Senior Development Officer, Children's Residential Care Unit, National Children's Bureau. It would not have been possible without a huge amount of help and support from a wide variety of sources. The key ones were:

- Department of Health, for funding the work
- The Policy Group of the Shared Care network for their endless input and patience. Members of the group are: Clare Waring, Jenny Bullock, Nick Loone, Jeanne Carlin, Rob Hawkins, Sean Broderick, Vicky Jones, Candy Smith and Fred Reynolds.

The critical readers for each chapter:

- Fiona Smith at the Royal College of Nursing, on Meeting Children's Care and Health Needs
- Beverley Dawkins at Mencap, on Moving and Handling, and Ivan Sharpe at Barnardo's on Behaviour Management and Physical Interventions.
- Vicky Jones, Director of Shared Care Network and Jeanne Carlin, Shared Care Network and freelance consultant, for reading and editing the document and making helpful comments.
- Sally Millar at the CALL Centre at Edinburgh University for kind permission to reproduce pages of communication passports in Chapter 6.

And lastly, but most importantly, to all those local statutory and voluntary sector agencies who sent us examples of forms and good practice. The fact that all the material is not reproduced here is not an indication of quality but of our need to select information to represent a process. We have tried to identify material wherever we can, but the sheer weight of material inevitably meant that some identifiers went astray. If this happened to you, we apologise.

This handbook marks the start of a process. We hope it will encourage you to continue with it.

Foreword

When the Disability Rights Commission was created, it set out a vision of 'a society where all disabled people can participate fully as equal citizens'. The past decade has unquestionably seen unprecedented progress in maximising the life chances of some disabled children and their families. We have moved beyond a negative and deficit-laden concept of disability to one where, hopefully, we celebrate and value disabled children's achievements and participation in communities where everybody belongs.

However, as the Prime Minister commented in his introduction to *Valuing People*, 'disabled children and their families still face many barriers to full participation in society'. In effect, there is still much work to do in narrowing the inequality gap and in ensuring that all disabled children do indeed have the quality of life anticipated in *Valuing People*, *Quality Protects*, *Every Child Matters*, the SEN Strategy and, of course, in the National Service Framework.

This handbook is essential reading for all service providers and (I hope) families – because 'risk' (however defined) has become one of the last taboos in taking forward the inclusion agenda and acknowledging disabled people's right to be treated with dignity and respect and receive the support they need for full inclusion in society.

There are around 8.6 million disabled people in the UK. The extent to which they feel valued and included will be profoundly affected by their experiences as children. As the handbook notes, a growing number of disabled children have complex disabilities or severe behavioural difficulties. But it is not only disabled children's impairments which determine the quality of their life – disabling attitudes and a disabling environment can result in unequal access to a wide range of community services and facilities. Everybody has the right to be safe – but inappropriate and over-zealous approaches to risk management can negate disabled children's life chances and have a long-lasting impact on their future development and achievements.

Poor practice in risk management usually relates to insecurity about what is safe and acceptable. For the first time, this handbook shares positive practice and experiences in risk management which benefit everybody. We cannot ignore risk purely for fear of future litigation. In the end, as a young disabled person said to me recently:

> 'The saddest words are "you can't", when you know that you can – I'm like a glass vase shut up in a cupboard where nobody sees me, because everybody thinks I might break if they got me out! I don't want to sue anyone if I have an accident – I just want to get a life!'

I hope and believe this handbook will help disabled children and young people, their families and carers to break the 'risk' taboo and, indeed, to 'get a life'.

Philippa Russell
Disability Rights Commissioner

1 Introduction

This chapter covers
Risk management: the context
Key principles underlying the handbook
How to use this handbook
References

Risk management: the context

The effective management of risk should be a concern for everyone who works with disabled children and their families. Increasing litigation and the compensation culture, coinciding with a time of increased complexity within the population of disabled children, are leading to the exclusion of disabled children from services on a daily basis. It is unforgivable that the position has been reached where disabled children are being excluded from disabled children's services because they are "too disabled".

Disabled children and their families should be fully included in society. This handbook is part of the move towards a citizenship agenda that has social inclusion at its heart. Appropriately, there is a rising interest in risk and risk assessment.

This handbook is designed to illustrate, and help services take, a proactive approach to risk management and ultimately to the inclusion of disabled children in everyday life. It is designed to be used by everyone who supports disabled children and their families.

Who are the children?

There are approximately 320,000 disabled children in England, the majority of whom live at home with their parents. The prevalence of severe disability and complex needs has risen in recent years. This is due to a number of factors, including the increased survival rate of babies born prematurely or with congenital abnormalities and the increased survival of children after severe trauma or illness.

There are up to 6,000 children living at home who are dependent on complex medical technology. There are also greater numbers of children recognised as having autistic spectrum disorders. In an in-depth analysis of disabled children's services, reported in the *Fourth Analysis of the Quality Protects Management Action Plans: Services for disabled children and their families* (Council for Disabled Children 2002), local authorities identified both of these groups as rising in numbers and as being the greatest challenge to service provision. This handbook looks at the needs of both these groups of children in relation to risk management. The children referred to are those with complex needs.

'Describing people's health and support needs as "complex" may be inappropriate, because there is a danger of treating someone's needs as the problem, whereas the problem is the barriers they experience to getting their needs met. Policy makers and professionals tend to use the term "complex health and support needs", but it is not really people's needs which are "complex"; rather, the systems and services that they have to negotiate to get their needs met are complex. A key common characteristic of children and young people who are described as having "complex health needs" is that they all require a combination of health and support services in order to access a good quality of life, and that existing services seem to find it complex to meet their needs.' (Jenny Morris 1999)

Current concerns about risk management

Reports and discussions suggest that the following current concerns about risk management have led to diverse practice in service delivery, including children with complex needs being denied a service.

Fear of liability
Staff fear they will be blamed if something goes wrong. They do not feel they are in a supportive environment where working with children with complex needs will be seen as positive. This extends to fears about working with staff from other professions.

Lack of insurance
Staff are not confident they will be adequately insured for their task. Insurance companies often view these children as "too risky", and the rise of a compensation culture, together with a loss of Crown immunity for NHS staff, compounds worries.

Lack of training
Staff in social care and education settings do not feel adequately trained to meet the needs of children with disabilities or special educational needs, and therefore feel unable to accept them into their services.

Cost
Children with complex needs require high levels of support. They are therefore "expensive". Little information is available on service costs. Caroline Glendinning's research constructed exemplar case studies to illustrate the wide range of medical, nursing and other needs of technology-dependent children. The costs of equipment and consumables, staffing costs and costs borne by families were calculated.

> 'For a child dependent on ventilation and fed by gastrostomy, average total annual costs to statutory services were £122,085. Additional costs of £1,030 (net of social security benefits) were borne by the family. For an infant with a tracheotomy and artificial feeding, average annual costs to statutory services were £29,432. Additional costs of £775 (net of social security benefits) were borne by the family.'
> (Glendinning et al 1999)

In an environment where finance is limited, arguments about who should bear the costs remain central to decisions about service provision. Changing definitions of health and social care add to an already confused picture. This was noted in the House of Commons report on children's health in the community in 1997 which stated:

> 'We are committed to reducing the current fragmentation of services between social services, health and education agencies ... there is a need for a new spirit of co-operation between the agencies which, together, provide services for children. It is important that the needs of the child or young person are met, and that disagreements about who provides a particular service or item of equipment should not disrupt the care of the child.'
> (HMSO 1997)

Direction and advice
Despite the 1997 House of Commons report, there remains a lack of direction and advice mandating local services to reach joint agreements. Mencap's report *Don't count me out* (Mencap 2001) describes how children with learning disabilities are excluded from education because of health needs. It is clear that 'uncertainty and confusion remain about whose responsibility it is to provide care for children with health needs at school'.

Lack of agreement on joint funding is further complicated by boundary issues. The difficulty in establishing tripartite funding for some specialist children's services and placements, and the differences of provision and funding nationally, reflect this further. There is a clear need for joint agreement on the management of risk, backed by joint protocols and joint financing; this may be met through Children's Trusts.

There is a lack of research into the specific difficulties of parents who have children with complex health needs or who are dependent on technology. Petr *et al* (1995) conducted research in the USA with parents of technology-dependent children which looked at their specific difficulties. These were identified as:

- finding suitably experienced carers
- finding adequate short breaks
- dealing with large quantities of paperwork
- sustaining support on a long-term basis.

Key principles underlying the handbook

There are certain principles which should underpin service provision and risk management. These are: inclusion, rights and partnership.

Inclusion

Disabled children, whatever the level or complexity of their impairment, should have a right to the same quality of life as all children. Inclusion of disabled children means that all services and the people in them need to change and develop so as to provide a high-quality service which can adapt to meet a range of needs. An inclusive service is one which embraces diversity. It leads to changes in mainstream services, rather than changes in disability services.

Rights

Entitlement
Disabled children have statutory rights to services under the Children Act 1989, Children (Scotland) Act 1995, the Northern Ireland Children Order 1995 and the Chronically Sick and Disabled Persons Act 1970.

According to the Children Act 1989 local authorities have a particular responsibility to provide a range of services and support for disabled children and their families which are designed to minimise the effects of disability and give them the opportunity to lead lives which are as 'as normal as possible' (Schedule 2, paragraph 3).

The Chronically Sick and Disabled Person's Act 1970 places various duties on local authorities with reference to disabled people of all ages, including disabled children. In particular, it requires a local authority to make arrangements to provide a number of services if it is satisfied that it is necessary to do so to meet a disabled person's needs. These services include: practical assistance in the home; facilities for, or assistance with, travelling to and from home; holidays; and provision or assistance in obtaining a telephone.

Access
A second source of statutory rights for disabled children is the Disability Discrimination Act 1995, which applies in England, Scotland and Wales. Separate secondary legislation and codes of practice are required in Northern Ireland, and Schedule 8 of the Act sets out the modifications that apply there. Part III of the Act sets out disabled people's rights when accessing goods and services. Disabled people must not be discriminated against by those providing goods, facilities or services to the public.

Since December 1996 it has been unlawful for service providers to:

- refuse to provide a service to a disabled person which they provide to other members of the public, or to a section of the public
- provide services of a worse standard
- provide service on less favourable terms.

In addition, since 1999 service providers must:

- change any policy, practice or procedure which makes it impossible or unreasonably difficult for a disabled person to use the service
- provide an auxiliary aid or service to enable a disabled person to make use of the service.

In September 2001 The Special Educational Needs and Disability Act brought Education into the Disability Discrimination Act.

By 2004 service providers may need to 'make reasonable adjustments in relation to the physical features of their premises in order to overcome physical barriers to access'.

In Scotland, issues are addressed through the Educational Needs and Disability 2001

(Scotland Act). Planning duties in Scotland have separate guidance and legislation through the Disability Strategies and Pupils Educational Records (Scotland Act 2002). The consultation period on the Special Educational Needs and Disability Bill in Northern Ireland ended in December 2002.

Childhood

A failure to adopt procedures which enable this group of children to gain equal access to services could lead to their being denied what they have a right to expect according to the 1989 United Nations Convention on the Rights of the Child (UNCRC). The UNCRC sets out three main areas of rights for all children: non-discrimination, best interests, and participation in decisions about their lives.

Partnership

Partnership with children

Policies should emphasise the fact that all disabled children can communicate, and the people working with them should finds ways of enabling them to do so. All new paperwork looking at children's needs should include a section on the child's views, with a minimal requirement to discuss how the child indicates both happiness and distress rather than the all-too-convenient statement, 'not applicable or not relevant'.

Developments through the Quality Protects programme show that the majority of services now recognise that disabled children can communicate and, more importantly, that they have something valuable to say. The development of communication materials and training packs has clearly helped to recognise the importance of this area.

A number of authorities are using *I'll go first* (Children's Society 1999) and finding it effective in terms of both work with individual children and also promoting awareness of communication methods in general. Two further sets of materials have a greater focus on children with complex needs, *Ask Us* (Children's Society 2002) and

Two Way Street (NSPCC/Triangle/JRF 2001) are beginning to demonstrate a huge potential for enhancing communication with disabled children.

Further information on materials available for working with disabled children is available at www.doh./integrated childrenssystem.

Partnership with families

Open and honest partnership with families is at the heart of managing risk. Service providers and families need a common understanding of *what* can be managed and *how* it will be managed. Parents can choose to manage risk in many ways but some of these options will not be open to service providers. Services will need to agree all risk management protocols with families and be honest and clear about their limitations.

Partnership between agencies

Effective services for children with complex needs are those which operate on an inter-agency basis. The Health Act 2000 and the further development of Children's Trusts set the legal framework for this to be formalised. Pooled budget and lead commissioning approaches to children with complex needs would at least begin to take away the arguments about who pays and could lead to a wider development of good practice initiatives. All risk protocols should be firmly embedded in a multi-agency approach, and services should ensure that protocols are agreed by the Disabled Children's Multi Agency Strategy Group.

How to use this handbook

The workbook is based mainly on the experience of Shared Care services and has been written primarily with these services in mind. It will therefore be particularly useful for providers of short-break services, in-home care such as sitting services, befriending schemes, playschemes, weekend leisure services, and after-school clubs. However, much of the policy and guidance is transferable to other settings and it will be of interest to schools and residential settings.

Each chapter outlines essential elements of good practice and policy, with references and examples of forms used by different service providers. The forms have been adapted for publication in this handbook. They can be photocopied and further adapted, and there are no restrictions on the use of material.

References

Council for Disabled Children (2002) *Fourth Analysis of the Quality Protects Management Action Plans: Services for disabled children and their families*

Jenny Morris (1999) *Hurtling into the Void*, Pavilion Publishing

Caroline Glendinning et al (1999) *The Community-Based Care of Technology Dependent Children in the UK: Definitions, numbers and costs*

HMSO (1997) *Health Services for Children and Young People in the Community, Home and School*, Third report

Mencap (2001) *Don't Count me Out: The exclusion of children with a learning disability from education because of health needs*

Petr *et al* (1995) reported in *Gastrostomy and Children: A review of the literature*, Children and Society 2001

Children's Society (1999) *I'll Go First: The planning and review kit for use with children with disabilities*

Children's Society (2002) *Ask Us* (CD-Rom), Commissioned by the Quality Protects Reference Group, *Ask Us 2* (CD-Rom), 2003

NSPCC/Triangle/JRF (2001) *Two Way Street*, a training video and handbook about communicating with disabled children and young people

2 Health and safety

This chapter covers
The definition of risk
Managing risk
Designing safe services
Common scenarios
Risk management and standards
References
Sample forms and guidance

The definition of risk

Disabled children and young people need support and protection so that they are not exposed to unacceptable risks. At the same time, their rights to develop and learn and to be included in all aspects of community life must be recognised.

As well as enabling disabled children and young people to enjoy the opportunities and experiences that all children do, service providers are responsible for assessing and managing risk to ensure they themselves are not reckless or negligent in the carrying out of their duties. Service providers also have duties and responsibilities under Health and Safety Regulations and National Minimum Standards to safeguard the health, safety and welfare of staff and carers. All the work of short break services carries an element of risk. This risk cannot be removed completely, but it is possible to manage it.

Risk refers to the possibility of a situation occurring which would involve exposure to danger or a hazard, that is, the possibility of something harmful happening. Risk is calculated from a basic formula that assesses:
- the likelihood of a hazard or injury
- the seriousness of the potential hazard or injury.

However, a hazard is less likely to cause *harm* if certain controls are in place. Controls are the steps taken either to eliminate the hazard or reduce the associated risk to an acceptably low level. Short break service providers must therefore manage the risk by assessing it, avoiding it if it is unnecessary and reducing it to a level which is 'reasonably practicable'. Risk management involves assessing the risk for each service user and taking the necessary action to manage that risk, while bearing in mind both the person who is undertaking the task and the child or young person receiving the service.

What is reasonably practicable?

Reasonably practicable, as defined by the Health and Safety Executive (HSE), means 'an employee has satisfied his/her duty if he/she can show that any further preventative steps would be grossly disproportionate to the further benefit which would accrue from their introduction'. (HSE 1992, p 8)

Managing risk

Providers of short break services will need to undertake risk assessments for the following:
- the safety and appropriateness of a carer's household
- each child's placement, both within a carer's home or the child's own home
- group activities and outings.

Additional risk assessment may be required for children with specific support needs, eg invasive care, intimate care, moving and handling, and behaviour management.

A risk assessment form (Form 1) and a checklist for assessing a carer's home (Form 2) are included at the end of this chapter.

Designing safe services

Short break service providers have a responsibility to ensure that children and young people are cared for as safely as possible, whether this is within a short break carer's home, the child's own home, a residential setting or a day care setting such as a playscheme or weekend scheme.

The care needs and abilities of children vary widely, therefore a risk assessment needs to be carried out for each individual child or young person, and for each service that they receive, as potential hazards will be different for each child and each setting.

A checklist of potential hazards can never be totally comprehensive, but clear advice must be given to carers on making their homes a safe and healthy environment for children. This will form part of the assessment process. It is equally important that the health and safety of a child's own home is risk assessed, if that is where the care is to be provided. A balance needs to be found between imposing health and safety requirements on a family and ensuring that an in-home carer, as well as the care she/he provides, is safe. It is therefore essential that services identify a budget to enable families to meet some basic safety requirements, for example, installing smoke alarms.

Quick guide to potential hazards

The following is intended as a quick guide to what might be considered as potential hazards. More detailed guidance can be found in the Shared Care Network booklet, *Safe and Healthy*, which was written primarily for short break carers (Shared Care Network 2001).

Within the home generally
The following should be checked:
• floors (Are they clear of clutter? Are they highly polished?)
• staircases
• doors (Do they have safety glass? Check the locks.)
• windows
• furnishings
• electrical fittings
• heating
• storage of poisonous and hazardous substances, eg cleaning materials, alcohol
• storage of dangerous objects, eg scissors, tools.

Within the kitchen
The following should be checked:
• hot objects, eg irons and kettles
• saucepans
• cookers
• sharp objects, eg knives
• fridges and freezers
• rubbish bins.

Within the bedroom
The following should be checked:
• cot mattresses
• cot sides
• bunk beds.

Within the bathroom
The following should be checked:
• slippery surfaces
• toilet
• storage of medication.

Within the garden
The following should be checked:
• steps
• play equipment
• ponds
• gates
• fencing
• sheds and garages
• greenhouses
• washing lines
• poisonous flowers and plants.

Fire safety
In every domestic setting where care is provided there should be a minimum of two smoke alarms carrying the kite mark and meeting British Standard BS5446. Alarms must be kept in working order.

It is also essential that care providers, including short break carers, have clearly planned escape routes in the event of a fire breaking out which have been practised with the children. It is important that carers providing a service in the child's own home are aware of aspects of safety.

Safety outside the home
When disabled children and young people are going to be taken on outings, either

individually by a short break carer or befriender, or as part of a group activity, a checklist should be made by the short break service of the kinds of hazards and considerations which need to be taken into account. Such considerations could include:

- clothing (appropriate for the weather, the activity)
- child's awareness of danger
- child's tolerance to certain situations (eg noise, overcrowding)
- safety of play equipment in parks, play areas, etc
- presence of qualified lifeguards when swimming (or similar for other activities)
- awareness of hygiene and safety when visiting farms and zoos
- sufficient medicine and all the equipment that the child needs is taken
- a mobile phone is available if there is any possibility that emergency help may be needed
- essential and emergency telephone numbers are to hand
- basic first aid skills are kept updated
- written consent has been obtained from parents for emergency or other medical treatment
- general written consent has been obtained from parents for a group outing
- a copy of risk assessment from place being visited.

Safety in the car

A list of important considerations when transporting children should include:

- checking the quality and suitability of car seats and harnesses
- checking that the person who will be driving has a valid driving licence, MOT certificate (where appropriate) and insurance that covers transporting children as part of their short break caring and/or employment
- checking that the vehicle is roadworthy and adequately maintained.

Equipment safety

Basic guidelines on a child or young person's equipment should include ensuring that:

- care providers are trained in the use of all specialist equipment
- equipment is kept clean and in good working order
- a child's equipment needs are regularly reviewed.

Legal responsibilities

Short break service providers have legal responsibilities to their employees under health and safety regulations. Employees are likely to include residential workers, leisure staff, befrienders, sitters and in-home care workers. The law provides different protection for people who are not employees, for example short break carers, but they can invoke compensation under the general law of negligence, as service providers have a 'duty of care' towards them (see next paragraph).

Guidance from the Borough of Poole's Shared Care Scheme (available from the Shared Care Network) defines 'duty of care' as follows:

Duty of care means the common law principle of the need to preserve life, health and well-being. If carers have undertaken a responsibility to provide care and protection they cannot simply stand by and do nothing in the knowledge that life-threatening consequences may follow. The actual obligation will depend on the situation: it may be to call for medical assistance or it may be to apply medical treatment where more appropriate personnel or advice is unlikely to be present in time to save the person from harm.

A duty of care is imposed on anyone who takes on the care of a 'helpless or infirm' person. If the duty of care is breached by a failure to take proper care then the civil liability of negligence may be raised. A gross breach of the duty of care could give rise to criminal proceedings.'

If an incident occurs in which a service user is harmed or in which a service user causes harm to someone else, then the provider of that service and its staff must be able to show they have assessed and managed the risk

The dignity of risk

correctly. In terms of the law, there are two charges that could be made against staff:

- **negligence** – where staff failed to do something which it was their duty to do, and a foreseeable loss resulted from this
- **recklessness** – where staff knew there was a risk, but either did not manage that risk or deliberately allowed the situation to occur in spite of the risk.

In answering either of the two charges, staff cannot claim they were unaware of a risk. They must prove that they assessed all relevant areas of risk and took adequate steps to minimise it and their actions were 'reasonably practicable' (see page 10 for definition).

In considering what carers can and cannot do, a distinction must be made between meeting needs which can be absorbed within the routine of normal family life, and those which are life-supporting or are of critical importance because they are focused on a child's exceptional care and support needs. This involves the duty of care and is relevant to the general responsibilities concerning the care of children and young people. It is important that carers have an understanding of the duty of care to ensure they know how to react in certain situations.

Common scenarios

Scenario 1
You have been providing a short break service to an 11-year-old boy who has cerebral palsy. The placement is successful and meets his needs. Recently, an occupational therapist visited him at home and advised that, as his moving and handling needs had changed, his short break carer should be provided with a sliding board. It will cost the service £40 to purchase this.

Clearly, this is a reasonable request and the provider should purchase the sliding board. This additional control is now required in order to prevent harm or injury to either the carer and the child. The purchase is reasonably practicable in that the cost is not grossly disproportionate to the further

benefit and the service could be deemed negligent or reckless in failing to purchase it.

Scenario 2
Three months ago you placed a nine-year-old girl who is on the autistic spectrum and presents behaviour that challenges. Her link family were enthusiastic during the introductory period and the early days of the placement, but you are concerned that their initial enthusiasm may be waning. They have now said they are willing to continue, but in order to deal with the girl's behaviour, they will need to fix new door and window locks throughout the house and erect a six-foot high fence around their garden.

There are a number of considerations here in managing risk. The cost of providing locks and a fence may be grossly disproportionate to the further benefit which would accrue from their introduction if the initial enthusiasm of the family is indeed waning, and this request may mask a desire on their part to end the link. Managing this risk would, therefore, require a further assessment of the link family's house and garden to assess the potential hazards as well as an assessment of the impact on the child's quality of life if the requests were granted. Additional training and guidance to the link family in managing the child's behaviour may be considered as a further control as well as a review of the child's behaviour management plan.

Scenario 3
A child who attends your Saturday scheme is fed via a naso-gastric tube. Two of the scheme workers have been trained in administering a feed. Half-way through a session, the tube becomes dislodged. The scheme workers are unable to get a response from the local Children's Community Nursing Team and so phone the child's mother as the child is due for a feed. The mother says she cannot get there and asks if one of the trained scheme workers could re-insert the tube.

Although the scheme workers will have been trained to administer a feed, they will not have received training on the re-insertion of the tube. This action is on the prohibited list for non-parent carers. Although the child is due for a feed, the risk to both the child and the staff member posed by re-insertion is greater than the feed being delayed. In this case, the scheme workers would either have to wait until the mother arrives or the local nursing team responded, or they could take the child to the local A&E department, basing their decision on what was likely to be the quickest response.

Risk management and standards

The Care Standards Act 2000 reformed the regulatory system for care services in England and Wales. Scotland's equivalent is the Regulation of Care (Scotland) Act 2001. There is currently no similar legislation applicable in Northern Ireland.

During 2001/02, independent public bodies were set up under these Acts to take over the regulation of social and health care services which had previously been regulated by local councils and health authorities. These regulatory bodies are:
- in England, the Commission for Social Care Improvement
- in Scotland, the Scottish Commission for the Regulation of Care
- in Wales, the Care Standards Inspectorate for Wales.

The regulatory remit of these bodies was extended to include other services not previously requiring registration, such as domiciliary care and fostering services. Due to the range and diversity of short break provision, services are now subject to a number of different standards, which can be summarised as follows:
- **Overnight short breaks with carers:** National Minimum Fostering Standards in England and Wales; National Care Standards for Foster Care and Family Placement Services in Scotland
- **Residential short breaks:** Children's Home National Minimum Standards in England and Wales; National Care Standards for Care Homes for Children and Young

People in Scotland
- **Sitting services and in-home care:** Domiciliary Care Standards (which include the provision of personal care) in England; Care at Home Standards in Scotland
- **Weekend/after-school clubs and playschemes:** Full Day Care or Sessional Day Care Standards in England and Wales if services include children aged eight and under; National Care Standards for Early Education and Childcare up to the age of 16 in Scotland.

An overview of the standards

A standard is a set of outcomes that providers should aim to achieve. Each standard has supporting criteria which give pointers, or performance indicators, as to how the standard might be met. All the standards that apply to short break services within England, Scotland and Wales include minimum requirements relevant to the three areas of risk management discussed in this handbook. These are: intimate and invasive care; moving and handling; and physical interventions and behaviour management.

All Scottish standards are based on five key principles which reflect recognised rights: dignity, privacy, choice, realising potential and safety. The right to safety includes the right to feel safe and secure in all aspects of life, including health and well-being, and to enjoy safety but not be over-protected. This approach to standards should ease the task of managing the fine balance between risk and rights in Scotland.

The following is a brief overview of the relevant standards. Compliance with them should form the baseline from which services develop good practice guidelines and policies.

Fostering Standards require services to promote and safeguard a child or young person's physical, mental and emotional welfare. Fostering services must make available carers who provide a safe, healthy and nurturing environment, and the preparation and training of foster carers must cover health and safety issues. Foster carers must also be provided with written

The dignity of risk

guidelines on their health and safety responsibilities. (See the Shared Care Network guidelines for carers *Safe and Healthy* and *Safe and Sound*.)

Children's Home Standards require that positive steps be taken to keep children safe from fire and other hazards. The registered person is required to regularly review the implementation and effectiveness of action identified as a result of risk assessments.

Domiciliary Care Standards in England state that the health and safety of service users and homecare and support workers is a major issue of concern in the provision of personal domiciliary care. Training on all aspects of health and safety is essential to ensure that home care and support staff are able to respond appropriately and work in a safe manner. Before commencing the provision of care in a new home, the organisation providing the service must carry out a detailed assessment of the risks associated with the delivery of the service. This assessment must be undertaken by someone who is trained for the purpose. The risk assessment must be comprehensive and include, where appropriate, the risks associated with assisting with medication as well as any risks associated with travelling to and from the home of the service user, particularly at night. A separate risk assessment must be undertaken of the risks associated with manual handling.

Sessional/Full Day Care Standards require premises to be safe, secure and suitable for their purpose. The provider must take positive steps to promote safety within the setting and on outings, and ensure that proper precautions are taken to prevent accidents.

Medical and clinical procedures

All the standards include performance indicators on medication and first aid training, which will provide services with a baseline for developing policy and guidelines for the provision of clinical and intimate care procedures.

Fostering Standards state that no placement should be made which prevents a child from continuing to receive the specialist health care services that they need. The foster carer must be provided with a full description of the health care needs of a child and clear procedures governing consent for the child to receive medical treatment. Foster carers must be provided with a written health record and fostering services must have good links with health agencies and help the foster carer to secure services for the child placed. Basic training for foster carers must include first aid.

Children's Home Standards in England and Wales cover children with complex health care needs more comprehensively than in Scotland. They require that staff who carry out skilled health tasks (eg catheter care, administration of oxygen or rectal diazepam and so on) should do so only on the written authorisation of the prescribing doctor or responsible nurse. There are also requirements for records to be kept of all such tasks and for prior written permission to be placed on file for the administration of first aid and appropriate non-prescribed medication. Children's homes must also have a policy, with written guidance, for storing, dispensing and administering medication, and the registered person must follow medical or nursing advice in a written protocol on the provision of non-prescribed household medicines. Any treatment which is prescribed must be included in the child's placement plan or care plan. Staff must be trained in first aid.

Domiciliary Care Standards in England and Care at Home Standards in Scotland include a specific standard on medication, where it is provided as part of the service. It requires that the provider has arrangements in place for medication to be provided safely and in the way that best suits the user. The English Domiciliary Care Standards require the registered person to have a clear, written policy and procedure which identifies parameters and circumstances for assisting with medication and health-related tasks and which also identifies assistance and tasks which may not be undertaken without specialist training. Staff should not provide assistance with taking or administering medication or undertake other health-related tasks unless it is within their competence and they have received the necessary specialist training. This kind of assistance must be identified in the care plan, form part of the risk assessment and be detailed within the service user plan. Care workers must record assistance in giving medication, including dosage and time, as well as any other health-related tasks.

Sessional Full Day Care Standards in England and Wales require the registered person to have a clear policy regarding the administration of medication. If medicine is to be given, it must be prescribed for a specific child by a doctor and the parent must give prior written permission. The standards also require that written records are kept of all medicines administered to children and parents must sign the record book to acknowledge the entry. If technical or medical knowledge is required, then individual training must be given to staff by a qualified health professional and the training must be specific to the individual child concerned. Providers must have first aid boxes on the premises and at least one staff member with a current first aid training certificate. There is also a requirement that the registered person ensures the privacy of children with special needs when intimate care is being provided. Scotland's standards require clear policy and guidelines on the use, storage and administration of medication and that staff are suitably trained.

Restrictive physical interventions

Fostering Standards contain no specific references to restrictive physical intervention, although the provision of training to foster carers on managing behaviour is a requirement.

Children's Home Standards stipulate that the policy on the use and techniques of physical restraint and the circumstances in which it may be used must be consistent with relevant national government guidance. All staff must be trained and supported in the use of restraint. English and Welsh

standards further require that staff have signed that they have the registered person's policy on restraint and that they have continued access to the policy. All standards for England, Scotland and Wales require that written records of the use of control, restraint or discipline must be kept both on the child's file and in a dedicated book.

Domiciliary Care Standards state that physical intervention is only to be used as a last resort, in accordance with Department of Health guidance. The use of physical intervention must protect the rights and best interest of the service user and should be the minimum which is consistent with safety. The personal service user plan must set out procedures in relation to the taking of risks in daily living; for service users who are likely to be aggressive or abusive or cause harm to themselves or others, procedures should focus on positive behaviour.

Sessional Full Day Care Standards applicable to England and Wales require the registered manager to produce a written policy on behaviour management which states the methods that will be used to manage children's behaviour. Furthermore, adults must not use any form of physical intervention, eg holding, unless it is necessary to prevent personal injury to the child, other children or an adult, or serious damage to property. All incidents must be recorded and parents informed of incidents on the day they occur. There is also a requirement that a named staff member within the setting has responsibility for behaviour management issues.

Moving and handling

Fostering Standards contain no specific references to moving and handling but foster homes are required to have equipment appropriate to the child's age, development and level of ability. If the foster carer is to provide transport, the fostering service must ensure it is safe and appropriate to the child's needs. Scottish standards also include a requirement to provide foster carers with information about adapting their home or vehicle.

The dignity of risk

Children's Home Standards for England and Wales require homes to provide sufficient and appropriate equipment such as lifts, hoists and wheelchairs, and that all such equipment is regularly serviced. Rooms used to accommodate disabled children must, if relevant, have sufficient space for manoeuvrability of wheelchairs and other specialised equipment. The standards also require premises to be assessed by an occupational therapist and that their recommendations are adhered to.

Domiciliary Care Standards require the registered person to ensure that a separate moving and handling assessment is undertaken by a member of staff who is trained for the purpose. A comprehensive plan must be drawn up in consultation with the service user and be included in the service user plan, which is reviewed annually or more frequently if necessary. A procedure must be in place for reporting new risks which arise, including defective appliances, equipment, fixtures or security of the premises. The name and contact number of the organisation responsible for providing and maintaining equipment must be recorded on the risk assessment. The registered manager must ensure that manual handling equipment is in a safe condition to use and that inspections by the manufacturers have taken place on time, and must, if necessary, remind the organisation providing the equipment that a maintenance check is due. The standards also require that two people, fully trained in current safe handling techniques and in the use of the relevant equipment are always involved in the provision of care when the need is identified from the manual handling risk assessment. The requirement that staff are trained in manual handling is included in these standards.

Sessional Full Day Care Standards contain no specific standards concerning moving and handling. However, Standard 10 is about special needs (including special educational needs and disabilities) and requires the physical environment to be, as far as is reasonable, suitable for disabled children. The registered person must consult with parents about a child's need for any special services and equipment.

References

Health and Safety Executive (1992) *Manual Handling Operations Regulations* (MHOR), HMSO

Shared Care Network (2001) *Safe and Healthy*, York Publishing

Shared Care Network (2001) *Safe and Sound*, York Publishing

Sample forms and guidance

The following is a list of forms included in this chapter, and what they are used for. The forms were supplied by different organisations and local authorities, and have been adapted for publication in this handbook. They are intended to be examples of good practice and can be copied or adapted for use by other organisations. Copies of originals can be obtained from Shared Care Network.

Form 1 Risk assessment. Barnardo's Rochdale Service

Form 2 An example checklist for assessing a carer's home. Barnardo's Family Link in Newham

Form 1

Barnardo's Rochdale Service

Basic details

Name of child/young person using the service _____

Date of birth _____

Address _____

_____

Areas requiring assessment of risk *(please circle all that apply)*

1 Home   **2** School   **3** Leisure   **4** College/education

5 Holiday   **6** Playgroup   **7** Other (please specify) _____

People who are involved in this risk assessment and who should be sent a copy of it

Name _____

Address _____

_____

Activities your service carries out with the child/young person

Go through the time the person is using your service from the time they begin the week to the end of the week, listing the activities they do, eg get up, go to toilet, get on bus, go in car or hang up their coat. Write each activity only once – it's just so that you remember to think of every activity the person does with your support. For any activity, if there is any risk that isn't being managed, tick the column next to it.

Activity: what, where, when, with whom	*Risk?*

     The dignity of risk

Checklists of activities

These checklists will help you and the parent double-check whether there are any risks to the child/young person or others when doing any activities. You should already have gone through the day and week, identifying anything that the child/young person does that might be risky. Put a tick in the appropriate column for each activity listed. Do not leave any item unmarked – if you do, it will appear that you have been negligent.

	Personal care activity	Not applicable/No opportunity	No risk or little risk	Significant risk
1	Eating			
2	Drinking			
3	Using the toilet			
4	Dressing/undressing			
5	Washing			
6	Bathing			
7	Showering			
8	Washing/brushing hair			
9	Brushing teeth			
10	Shaving			
11	Dealing with menstruation			
12	Choosing clothes			
13	Putting on makeup			
14	Dealing with own bodily fluids			
15	Changing incontinence pad			
16	Taking medication or undergoing required medical treatment or other physical health tasks			
17	Maintaining mental health			

The sort of risks include physical damage to the person, others or property through falling, choking, poisoning, infection and illness, malnutrition, dehydration, pain, overeating or over-drinking, self-injury, overdosing, suicide, and neglecting to do the activity properly. Risks also include social risks through unpleasant odours, looking odd to others, personal embarrassment, depression, etc. There may be risks of injury to staff, for instance when lifting, or risks due to the child/young person's behaviour in these situations, eg blocking toilets, taking clothes off, eating inedible substances, or risks due to the client neglecting to carry out the behaviour adequately.

	Domestic activity	Not applicable/No opportunity	No risk or little risk	Significant risk
1	General tidying up			
2	Bed making			
3	Vacuuming			
4	Sweeping/dusting/polishing			
5	Cleaning bathroom			
6	Cleaning kitchen			
7	Washing up			
8	Emptying bins			
9	Preparing hot and cold drinks			
10	Using knives/tin openers, etc			

Domestic activity	Not applicable/No opportunity	No risk or little risk	Significant risk
11 Food preparation/cooking			
12 Meal planning			
13 Food storage			
14 Washing clothes			
15 Ironing			
16 Using gas/electric fires and central heating			
17 Turning off appliances			
18 Locking up/making home secure			
19 Coping with emergencies and the unexpected (eg, power cuts)			
20 Looking after pets			
21 Budgeting/dealing with mail			
22 Maintenance of furniture, furnishings, fabric of building			

The sorts of risks include physical damage to the person, others or property through infections and diseases, assaults, fires, floods, explosions, electrocution, hypothermia, scalding, cuts, malnutrition, physical assault, etc, as well as social and emotional risks such as putting off others from visiting, looking odd, causing arguments between people, feeling frustrated and being exploited. The risk may be caused by neglecting to carry out the activity adequately or through challenging behaviour, eg losing their temper.

Community activity	Not applicable/No opportunity	No risk or little risk	Significant risk
1 Using public transport, eg buses, trains			
2 Using taxis			
3 Making journeys – familiar and unfamiliar			
4 Going out for walks			
5 Crossing roads			
6 Using leisure facilities, eg pub, cinema, sports centres			
7 Using health/social welfare facilities, eg GP, dentist, optician, hospital, chiropodist			
8 Using public facilities, eg toilets, bank, post office			
9 Shopping for clothes, groceries, household goods, etc			
10 Getting to school, work, day occupation			
11 Paying bills, handling own money			
12 Using pay and private phone			
13 Dialling emergency services			
14 Using a car			
15 Using community centres and other buildings			

The sorts of risks include physical damage to the person and to others, eg getting knocked over by a vehicle, hypothermia, malnutrition, getting attacked, not getting necessary health care or emergency treatment as well as social and emotional risks, eg anxiety, frustration, exploitation, isolation, boredom, annoying others, poverty and debt. The risks may be caused by neglecting to carry out the activity adequately or through challenging behaviour such as shouting in public, calling emergency services unnecessarily, nuisance phone calls.

	Social activity	Not applicable/No opportunity	No risk or little risk	Significant risk
1	Having and making friendships			
2	Relationships with staff/service users			
3	Sexual relationships			
4	Relationships with neighbours			
5	Relationships with family			
6	Contact with officials			
7	Contact with strangers			
8	Contact with children			
9	Contact with shopkeepers/milkmen, etc			
10	Contact with sales people calling/ phoning house			
11	Smoking			
12	Drinking alcohol			
13	Drug taking			

The sorts of risks include physical damage to the person, others or property through overdose, physical or sexual assault, pregnancy, diseases and medical problems. There might be social and emotional consequences such as stress, fear, confrontation, frustration, loneliness, exploitation, low self-esteem, confusion, involvement of police and public objections. There may be risks through neglecting to carry out the activity adequately or through challenging behaviour, such as insulting other people.

	Other activities *please list*
1	
2	
3	
4	
5	
6	

Detailed risk assessment

Complete one of these forms for each identified area of risk which needs a detailed assessment.

Information about the risk

1 What is the activity that you have identified as having a possible risk?

_____

2 What are the possible risks to the child/young person? (Please give details of what might happen, under what circumstances, the likelihood of this happening and the possible consequences for the person. State the evidence for your conclusions.)

_____

_____

_____

3 What are the possible risks to other people? (Please give details of what might happen, under what circumstances, the likelihood of this happening and the possible consequences for other people. State the evidence for your conclusions.)

_____

_____

_____

4 Are there any other risks, eg, to property? (What are they? Under what circumstances or how likely are they to happen? What are the possible consequences? State the evidence upon which your conclusions are based.)

_____

_____

_____

5 What are the potential benefits to the child/young person of carrying out the risky activity? (To be considered in order to get a balanced view of the benefits versus the risks.)

_____

_____

_____

6 What are the views of those involved?

Person _____

_____

Family _____

_____

Professionals (state who) _____

_____

Others (please specify) _____

_____

The dignity of risk

Proposed action plan

1 Action to be taken to prevent/reduce risk. (Please state who is responsible for what action and timescales.)

_____

_____

_____

2 Action to be taken if the risk occurs. (Please state who is responsible for what and timescales.)

_____

_____

_____

3 What, if any, is the residual risk? (ie, what is the remaining risk if the action plan is followed?)

_____

_____

_____

Risk assessment review form

This form is completed some time after the rest of the form has been completed. This risk assessment review should occur as agreed, at least annually as part of the Personal Plan or earlier if circumstances indicate there may be unmanaged risk. If any increase or change in the nature of risk is noted on this form, then you need to complete a new Risk Assessment Record Form.

1 *Basic details*
Name of person using the service _____

Date of birth _____

Address _____

_____

2 Date of last risk assessment or risk assessment review _____

3 Has there been any significant change in circumstances (eg change of home, respite, day service – including work, leisure, college, etc)

Yes/no (circle as appropriate)

If yes, give details _____

_____

4 Has there been any change in potential risk (either less risk or increased risk?)
(circle as appropriate)

No change in risk   Yes, less risk   Yes, increase in risk   Other

Please give details if there has been change _____

_____

_____

5 Is a full reassessment of risk required?

Yes/no (circle as appropriate)

6 Any other comments? _____

_____

_____

7 People involved in this review (please list)

_____

_____

8 Any others to whom copies of this review form should be sent? (please list)

_____

_____

9 Details of this risk assessment review

_____

_____

_____

_____

Name of person completing this risk assessment review form

Job title _____

Date completed _____

Next review of the risk assessment _____

Establishment/agency

Who will do what? _____

Date _____

Endorsement by line manager

Job title _____

Name of line manager _____

Signed _____

Establishment/agency _____

Comments _____

_____

_____

Date _____

Form 2

Barnardo's Family Link in Newham

Name	OK	N/a	Date checked	Further requirements/ comments	Date re-checked
Stairs (staircases and landings) Must be safely enclosed ie not open plan and not glass, and width between banisters no more than 3.5 inches/8.5 cms apart **Stairgates** Must be used particularly for under-3s and children of any age who have no sense of danger.					
Heating (gas/electric/Calor gas heaters) Must be BSI approved Must have fixed fireguards Radiators must have appropriate guard protection Paraffin/oil heaters are NOT allowed **Open fires** Must have fixed fire guards					
Sockets, plugs and electric equipment Safely wired plugs/safety plugs must be used Electrical sockets must have socket covers The wiring of any electrical equipment to be used in the child's bedroom must be checked					

In the kitchen

Electric kettle Short flex out of reach or coiled flex					
Worktop appliances Short flex or coiled flex					
Sharp knives In drawer with childproof lock					
Household cleaners In childproof cupboard					
Paracetamol, multi-vitamins, iron tablets, etc Locked away					
Saucepan handles On cooker kept turned away					
Matches Locked away					
Beware Highly polished floors No hanging table cloth on kitchen table					
Chest freezers Must be kept locked					

Health and safety

Name	OK	N/a	Date checked	Further requirements/ comments	Date re-checked

Washing machines/dryers
Doors to be kept closed

Cupboards
Where tools, DIY equipment, paint, etc
stored must be kept locked

Living/dining rooms
No tablecloths hanging down from tables
Glass topped tables to be removed whilst a
mobile child is in placement

Ornaments and valuables
Kept out of reach

Alcohol
Kept out of reach

Matches
Locked away

Household plants
Which can poison or cause nasty irritation if eaten/
handled by children, eg dieffenbachia (dumb cane or
leopard lily) should be kept out of reach

Garage
Must be kept locked, particularly if accessible from house

Access to garden and safety within it
- Securely fenced
- Locked gate
- No rubbish, eg rusty metal, old wood
- Ponds must be securely covered
- Gardens tools and pesticides must be kept in
  locked shed
- Beware of short stakes in flower beds
- Beware plants that are poisonous if eaten by children,
  eg lupin, foxglove, laburnum, delphinium, monkshood,
  deadly nightshade or rue or those which may cause
  irritation, eg euphorbia/spurge
- Dog/cat faeces

In the car
- Link children must travel in the back of the car in
  BS approved car seats, or special needs car seat
  or in harness or rear seat belts
- Carers must have car insurance

General
Smoke alarm
A smoke alarm on each level (carers to replace
batteries when required)

House insurance
- Carer has home contents insurance
- Carer has buildings insurance

The dignity of risk

3 Meeting children's health care needs

This chapter covers
Intimate and personal care
Invasive care
Policy framework needed to ensure service provision
Policy guidance: what needs to be in place?
Conclusion
References
Checklist of key points: invasive clinical procedures
Sample forms and guidance

Intimate and personal care

Disabled children and young people should be able to participate in all aspects of community life and it may be necessary for staff and carers to carry out intimate care procedures in a variety of settings. Children requiring intimate and personal care will vary in age, background and ethnicity, and will have differing levels of need, ability and communication skills. However, what they have in common is the right to be treated with sensitivity and respect and in such a way that their experience of intimate and personal care is a positive one.

Short break service providers should operate according to good practice guidelines for the provision of intimate and personal care. These should be an integral part of all child protection procedures.

What is intimate care?

Intimate care encompasses areas of personal care which most people usually carry out for themselves but some people are unable to do so because of an impairment or disability. Disabled children and young people might require help with eating and drinking or other aspects of personal care such as washing, dressing and toileting. Some may

also require help with changing colostomy or ileostomy bags, managing catheters or other appliances, and some may require the administration of rectal medication on occasions.

Principles of intimate care

Intimate care can be a positive experience for both the staff or carer and the child. It is essential that care is given gently and sensitively and that every child or young person is treated as an individual. As far as possible, the child should be allowed to exercise choice and should be encouraged to have a positive image of her/his own body.

These principles of intimate care can be put into practice by:
- allowing the child, wherever possible to choose who provides their intimate care
- encouraging the child to say if they find a carer unacceptable
- allowing the child a choice in the sequence of care
- ensuring privacy appropriate to the child's age and the situation
- allowing the child to care for her/himself as far as possible
- being aware of and responsive to the child's reactions.

Given the right approach, intimate care can provide opportunities to teach children about the value of their own bodies, to develop their personal safety skills and to enhance their self-esteem. Wherever children can learn to assist in carrying out aspects of intimate care they should be encouraged to do so.

Good practice in intimate care

Providing intimate and personal care places staff and carers in a position of great trust and responsibility. They are required to attend to the safety and comfort of the child or young person and must ensure that he/she is treated with dignity and respect. Activities related to intimate care should offer opportunities for the young person's personal development and choice. Even the youngest children can be encouraged to become aware of and value their own bodies and extend their personal skills and communication.

Wherever possible, intimate care provided to children up to the age of 12 should be carried out by a staff member or carer of the same gender. For teenagers and young people, intimate care should *always* be provided by carers of the same gender except in emergency or life-threatening situations. The religious and cultural values of children and their families must also be taken into account.

The following positive approaches will assist in promoting good practice for intimate care:

- carers should get to know the child well beforehand in other contexts and be familiar with her/his moods and methods of communication
- carers should speak to the child personally by name so that he/she is aware of being the focus of the activity
- carers should have knowledge and understanding of any religious and cultural sensitivities related to aspects of intimate care in respect of an individual child and take these fully into account
- carers should enable the child to be prepared for and to anticipate events while demonstrating respect for her/his body, eg by giving a strong sensory clue such as using a sponge or pad to signal intention to wash or change
- carers should ensure that the child or young person's privacy and modesty is respected and protected
- carers should agree with the child and their family appropriate terminology for private parts of the body and functions
- carers must always speak to older children in a way that reflects their age
- carers should keep records which note a child's responses to intimate care and any changes in behaviour.

Safe and Sound (Shared Care Network 2001) covers this in greater detail and provides further information for carers.

While many disabled children need assistance with intimate care, there are also a growing number of children with invasive care needs. The following section looks at the issues around children with complex health care needs and makes suggestions for producing a consistent policy.

Invasive care

During the early 1990s, there began to be a steady rise in the numbers of disabled children living in the community with greater complexities of health care needs. Referrals of such children to short break schemes led to growing concerns by service managers about the challenges and risks involved.

As there were no nationally agreed policies, guidelines or procedures covering the provision of invasive clinical procedures within short break services at that time, concerns about safe service delivery were justified, and insurance and liability issues were uncertain and unclear. Both Barnardo's (the leading provider of short break services in the voluntary sector) and Shared Care Network (the umbrella organisation for short break schemes in England, Wales and Northern Ireland) were keen to be proactive in formulating a policy that would enable these children to be included in service provision rather than excluded because of being too great a risk.

Children with complex health care needs

In the early 1990s, this group of children were typically referred to as 'medically fragile' or 'technologically dependent', terms which were clearly unacceptable both from a children's rights perspective and within the social model of disability. The term 'complex health care needs' was therefore introduced. Children with complex health care needs were defined as: 'Children and young people who are dependent on their parent or carer

The dignity of risk

carrying out an invasive clinical procedure which is essential, either as part of their routine care, or within an expected emergency situation.'

This definition covered the two main sets of circumstances in which administration of clinical procedures might be necessary:

- routine and regular care, eg nasogastric, gastrostomy and jejunostomy feeding, oxygen dependency, catheterisation, nebulising and suction processes, tracheotomy and stoma care
- emergency situations which are expected from time to time because of a long-term condition, for example, the use of rectal Valium or diazepam to control epilepsy.

There is no comprehensive data on the number of children with complex needs, although anecdotal and practice information indicates rising numbers. The primary reasons for the rise in complex health care needs are summarised in recent research by Caroline Glendinning *et al* (1999):

'**Medical advances** These have enabled severely impaired or very premature babies to survive infancy; improved the prognosis of children with life-threatening illnesses; and improved the health status of children with chronic illnesses. These developments mean that more children survive and that they are likely to survive for considerably longer than was previously the case.

Technological developments These have enabled cheaper, portable, compact, and easily operated/monitored technical devices to be developed which can be accommodated within domestic settings and operated by trained lay people rather than only by professional experts in hospitals.

Policy developments Since the early 1980s, long-term institutional care has been discouraged, particularly for children; professional changes have also emphasised the importance of involving parents as partners in their children's nursing care. Children with very complex needs now routinely access a wide variety of education settings.'

A paediatrician working with a short break scheme pointed out that:

'For infants born at 23 weeks gestation, 50 per cent will live and 50 per cent will die. Of the 50 per cent who survive, 50 per cent of them will be left with a long-term disabling condition.' (Personal communication, Lenehan 1997)

Policy framework needed to ensure service provision

Information obtained from Barnardo's short break services and Shared Care Network during the early 1990s indicated that service managers' concerns about invasive care for children with complex health care needs fell under four broad headings:

- fear of litigation
- uncertainty about the extent of insurance cover for short break carers carrying out a clinical procedure
- lack of clarity about training and support on clinical procedures for short break carers
- the absence of nationally agreed guidelines, policy or procedures.

It soon became evident that short break services throughout the UK were facing the same issues and challenges but, alarmingly, a number of local authorities were already addressing the issue by refusing to provide services for this group of children. The need for a policy framework had therefore become more urgent as the rights of children to fully participate in community life were clearly not being upheld.

Further investigation showed that central to the concerns and reluctance to provide services was insurance advice and the fear of legal liability and litigation. It therefore became clear that the formulation of policy guidance needed to start with insurance.

Insurance cover

The advice from insurance officers was always the same: short break carers would be covered to administer clinical procedures providing that all reasonable steps had been taken, as is the case with any risk activity. What needed to be established then, was what were the reasonable steps that needed to be taken when providing short break services to children with complex health care needs.

The breakthrough came when it was realised that the process of taking all reasonable steps was a circular one. It needed to include basic training and detailed written information prior to and during the matching and linking processes, followed by specific training, review and monitoring. Once this process was established, then insurance and legal liability was covered, and it became easier to begin to put the practice elements into place.

Influencing and lobbying

However, resolving insurance and liability issues was clearly not enough to dispel concerns across the UK. A lobbying and influencing strategy was therefore formulated to run alongside the development of a good practice model. There were two significant developments within this strategy which promoted the development and formulation of policy guidance.

First, the paediatric nursing advisor at the Royal College of Nursing (RCN) agreed to work on the production of lists of permitted and prohibited tasks for non-parent carers, such as short break carers, and to look at issues relating to inter-agency co-operation. These lists, which are regularly updated, are included within the policy guidelines *Towards a Healthy Future* and *Promoting Partnerships* and cover a wide range of clinical procedures that non-parent carers can administer following specific training (see box).

The re-insertion of nasogastric and gastrostomy feeding tubes was a grey area when the permitted and prohibited task lists were initially agreed. However, advice from the RCN has since clarified that neither nasogastric or gastrostomy feeding tubes should be re-inserted by a non-parent carer. Emergency back-up procedures must

Permitted tasks

- Administering prescribed medicine in a pre-measured dose via a nasogastric tube or gastrostomy tube
- Feeding through a nasogastric or gastrostomy tube
- Bolus feeds via a gastrostomy
- Pump feeds via a gastrostomy
- Bolus nasogastric feeds
- Tracheostomy care including suction and emergency change of tracheostomy tube
- Injections (intramuscular or subcutaneous) with a pre-assembled pre-dose loaded syringe
- Intermittent catheterisation and catheter care
- Care of a Mitrofanoff
- Stoma care
- Inserting suppositories or pessaries with a pre-packaged dose
- Rectal medication with a pre-packaged dose
- Manual evacuation
- Emergency treatments as covered in basic first aid training
- Assistance with inhalers, insufflation cartridges and nebulisers
- Assistance with oxygen administration
- Basic life support/resuscitation

Prohibited tasks

- Non-prescribed medicine except on parental instruction (staff or carers may not know whether the medication may react with other medication being taken)
- Re-insertion of a nasogastric tube
- Re-insertion of gastrostomy tube
- Injections involving: assembling syringes, administering intravenously or controlled drugs
- Programming of syringe drivers
- Filling of oxygen cylinders

[agreed by Barnardo's and the Royal College of Nursing, 2004]

therefore be agreed and written down in the individual health care plan, setting out the arrangements for the re-insertion of a feeding tube, should it become dislodged.

The lists provide basic guidance; new situations not covered by it should be considered on an individual clinical basis.

The second development was in 1997 when Barnardo's was invited to provide oral and written evidence to the House of Commons Select Committee on Health Services for Children in the Community: Home and School. The committee found it difficult to understand why issues remained unresolved and the Hansard recording of proceedings, produced below, became a key tool in working with health care professionals who were concerned about liability issues.

Health care staff were concerned that if they gave advice and training and a difficulty arose, they would not be covered through insurance by their employers and would be personally liable for any subsequent court action. The Hansard statement (HMSO 1997) makes it clear that the responsibility for providing such insurance lies with health care employers not with individual health staff.

'It is not acceptable that any health professional should be prevented from giving training to other carers through fear of litigation or through confusion as to his or her legal liability. We recommend that the DoH issue clarification to health authorities and trusts on this matter. In particular, we believe it should be made clear that the training of parents and non-parent carers by health care professionals is an important part of the work of the NHS. Those who are involved in it should be indemnified accordingly, either by the employing NHS body or (possibly more cost-effectively) by the NHS centrally (which could either self-insure or take out actual insurance).

We also recommend that the DoH should examine and clarify the legal position of non-parent carers, especially formal carers such as teachers and those providing respite care. As this kind of formal care can greatly reduce the burden on the NHS, by reducing the need for care to be given by health professionals, it does not seem intrinsically unreasonable that the NHS should bear the cost of indemnifying these individuals.' (HMSO 1997, p.xxxi)

Producing a policy

The coming together of practice and lobbying issues enabled policy guidance to be produced in 1998 in two publications: *Promoting Partnerships* published by Barnardo's and *Towards a Healthy Future* by Shared Care Network. These guides included reassurances to local authorities and voluntary agencies that they contained all the key policy and practice steps that needed to be in place.

The formulation and development of the policy originated from the need for a framework for short break carers, and even prior to publication, the range of services offered under the heading of 'short breaks' was already widening. In recent years, there has been ever greater diversity and creativity in short break provision and in particular, an increase in leisure-based services and in-home care. The policy and guidance contained within *Promoting Partnerships* and *Towards a Healthy Future* are applicable to all non-parent carers and should be followed as good practice in all forms of short break care for children and young people with complex health care needs.

Policy guidance: what needs to be in place?

Service providers should attempt to cover all the following areas in their policies on the provision of intimate and personal care and invasive care to disabled children with complex health care needs.

Written agreements and protocols

It is recommended that short break services have written joint agreements and protocols with their local primary care trust which set out how the agencies will work together to comply with policy guidelines on children with complex health care needs. Experience has shown that many schemes have successfully operated on an informal basis with key health professionals. However, these informal arrangements easily break down when key personnel change or move posts, leaving schemes without formally agreed input and support from their local trust.

In view of the changing nature of short break provision and the complexity of children's needs, it is recommended that written agreements and protocols are regularly reviewed and updated.

It is also recommended as good practice that schemes have an additional written agreement with non-parent carers who carry out clinical procedures, setting out the additional risks and responsibilities involved.

Detailed information on children

The service must have detailed written information about a child's medical condition and long-term health care needs. It is recommended that a child health profile form, a parent-led record which is verified by a medical practitioner, is completed for all children and young people. This record must be updated on a regular basis – every six months for children aged two and under and annually for children and young people aged two to 18 are suggested as good practice. These are, of course, required timescales for children and young people who have overnight stays with short break carers.

Health care plan

It is essential to have a written health care plan for each child or young person who requires invasive treatment or a clinical procedure. The plan should include instructions on the specific procedure and information for dealing with an emergency situation. The plan must be drawn up in conjunction with a health care professional and approved by a doctor or a nurse from the Children's Community Nursing Service or

School Health Service. The health care plan should be reviewed and updated annually.

Written consent

Prior written consent from parents must be given for any medication to be given to, or clinical procedure carried out on, a child or young person. Wherever possible, the child or young person should also give their written consent, with a minimal requirement that the child's views and methods of communication are discussed and recorded, as well as the specific words or signs that the child uses to indicate if there is a problem or discomfort during the administration of the medication or procedure.

The requirement on written consent contained within *Towards a Healthy Future* and *Promoting Partnerships* has led to improved practice in the general area of consent to medication and emergency medical treatment for all children on short break schemes. It highlighted a need for clarity on issues such as non-prescribed medication, for example Paracetomol, and the administration of medication which is not regularly taken, for example a course of antibiotics.

Basic training

All non-parent carers who provide short breaks to disabled children must receive basic training prior to starting a link or working in a service. Attendance is mandatory at training sessions in the three areas of first aid, child resuscitation, and moving and handling. These sessions should be provided alongside core training on child protection, etc. The sessions must be delivered by an accredited trainer and cannot be cascaded. Records of training received should be kept by service providers so that they are easily available for inspection purposes, and certificates of attendance should issued. Opportunities to refresh and update the training must be regularly provided: the suggested minimum requirement for training in all three areas is two years.

Individual training plan

All service providers must draw up an individual training plan for a non-parent carer who is going to carry out an invasive clinical procedure on a particular named child. The training plan must be agreed by the service manager, the non-parent carer who is to receive the training, and the health care professional who is going to provide the training.

Specific training

All non-parent carers who agree to carry out invasive procedures must receive child-specific training for each procedure that they will be required to undertake. There must be a written record of the training provided and the record must include a signed statement by the health care professional who provided the training, to say the person is competent to carry out the procedure on which they have been trained, for a named child. The signing of competency has remained a key issue, before during and even since the policy formulation process, as legal liability still concerns some nursing staff. Where the word 'competent' remains a sticking point, different forms of acceptable wording have been devised – 'skills appropriate to the needs of my patient' being one example.

The use of parents as trainers for non-parent carers in the administration of clinical procedures is totally unacceptable in terms of insurance and legal liability, the health, safety and welfare of the child or young person, and in placing unreasonable expectations and responsibilities on parents. However, parents remain their child's key communicators and advocates and the basis of training should be openness and honesty with parents and a partnership approach. It is therefore recommended that wherever possible, specific training takes place in the child's own home, as this is likely to be more acceptable and comfortable for the child and promotes partnership with the parents.

Written information

Non-parent carers should be provided with clear, written information on the child's medical condition, written information on the invasive procedure to be followed, for example, a fact sheet in the care provider's first language, and written information on the regular medication to be administered. This should include what the medication is, its strength and what it is for, when and how it is to be administered, and any side effects. This information must then be verified by the child's GP.

It is important that care providers, parents and children and young people understand that non-parent carers are not allowed to deviate from what is written on the medication sheet unless they have a signed letter from the child's GP or paediatrician confirming the change.

Medication sheets or written information on medication must be updated regularly, once a year as a minimum, but more frequently if there are changes in medication.

There are examples of medication sheets at the end of this chapter as well as example fact sheets on home gastrostomy feeding, nasogastric feeding, administration of adrenaline using an Epipen, and a checklist for administering rectal diazepam.

Written records

Non-parent carers must keep written records of the administration of medication and clinical procedures. Some carers record these in the communication book or service diary, while other services have developed specific medication recording sheets. The Care Standards Act 2000 places greater emphasis on the need for and quality of recording, and so systems for recording the administration of medication need to be sufficiently robust for inspection as well as safety purposes.

Review of competency

As with all procedures or guidelines, regular monitoring and review is an essential prerequisite. *Towards a Healthy Future* recommends that the competency of a non-parent carer in the particular clinical procedure on which they have been trained should be monitored and reviewed by the health care professional who provided the training. Therefore, systems need to be in place to ensure that a review is triggered automatically, at least once a year. This could, for example, be done at the annual foster care review for short break carers, or at the annual staff appraisal for sitters or in-home care staff.

It is also important to ensure that arrangements are in place to ensure earlier monitoring and review if required, for example if the child's medical condition has changed or if it is some time since the non-parent carer carried out the emergency procedure.

Conclusion

The policy guidance concerning provision of services to children and young people with complex health care needs is clearly laid out in *Towards a Healthy Future* and *Promoting Partnership*; the risks posed by the care of this group of children can therefore be reasonably managed. The Health Act 1999 introduced partnership flexibility, to bring health and social care agencies closer together and avoid traditional divides. One of the key elements of the government's social policy agenda is improved co-ordination of provision and joint working across health and social care, and this is central to all recent legislation, initiatives and strategies.

Despite these opportunities, implementation of *Promoting Partnerships* and *Towards a Healthy Future* throughout the UK still remains patchy, with evidence of continued reluctance from some health care trusts to enter into written agreements and protocols. The right for all children to participate fully in community life therefore continues to be violated, and the process of influencing and lobbying through good practice and training must continue.

Finally, we must constantly challenge the concept that disabled children are a fixed population, rather than a changing one. There must be a continual process of re-assessing the changing profile of disabled children, so that their needs are met. While, again, there are no accurate figures, anecdotal evidence from short break schemes indicates that the health care needs of children over the past decade have become more complex and challenging. For example, children who require long-term ventilation were not seen in short break services a decade ago, but this group are now increasing in number and predicted to rise. We constantly need to review the profile of children within the community, and their needs. While the needs of a small minority of children may yet prove to be too complex, we must continue to evaluate what reasonable steps we can take to minimise risk and ensure that all children who can be included, are included.

References

Shared Care Network (2001) *Safe and Sound*, York Publishing

Caroline Glendinning *et al* (1999) *The Community-Based Care of Technology Dependent Children in the UK: Definitions, numbers and costs*

Christine Lenehan (1997) Personal communication

Servian R, Jones V, Lenehan C, and Spires S for Shared Care Network (1998) *Towards a Healthy Future: Multi-agency working in the management of invasive and life-saving procedures for children in family based services*, Bristol: The Policy Press

Rhodes A, Lenehan C and Morrison J (1999) *Promoting Partnerships*, Barnardo's

HMSO (1997) *Health Services for children and young people in the community, home and school*, Third report, p 314

This chapter also draws heavily on materials from:

Helping Hands: Guidelines for staff who provide intimate care for children and young people with disabilities.

A project funded by the Scottish Office Education and Industry Department (1999)

The dignity of risk

Checklist of key points: invasive clinical procedures

1   Draw up written **agreements and protocols** with health commissioners and providers.

2   Obtain detailed written **information on the child or young person**.

3   Draw up a **written health care plan** in conjunction with a health care professional.

4   Obtain **written consent from parents** and **record communication methods of the child or young person**.

5   Provide **basic training** in first aid, child resuscitation and moving and handling to all non-parent carers.

6   Draw up an **individual training plan** in conjunction with the carer/staff member and the health care professional who is going to provide the training.

7   Arrange **child-specific training** for non-parent carers on each procedure that they will be carrying out and obtain a **signed statement** from the health care professional who provides the training.

8   Provide **written information** on the child's medical condition, all regular medication and the clinical procedure to be carried out.

9   Ensure systems are in place for non-parent carers to keep **written records** of clinical procedures and the administration of medication.

10 Carry out a regular **review and audit** of the non-parent carer's competence in the clinical procedure.

Sample forms and guidance

Forms and guidance in relation to invasive care are relatively well developed. The handbook brings together a selection of good practice forms from around the UK. Other areas of risk management are not as well developed and the shortage of best practice material reflects this.

   The following is a list of forms included in this chapter, and what they are used for. The forms were supplied by different organisations and local authorities, and have been adapted for publication in this handbook. They are intended to be examples of good practice and can be copied or adapted for use by other organisations. Copies of originals can be obtained from Shared Care Network.

Form 1 An example of a contract between agencies clarifying responsibilities. York Sharing Care Scheme

Form 2 An example of a contract from a trust where the integrated health and social service system particularly supports collaborative working. Craigavon and Banbridge Community Health and Social Service Trust

Form 3 A detailed agreement between Shared Caring and carers on the Additional Health Needs Scheme. It provides a clear example of the additional risks and responsibilities, and the accompanying support mechanisms, for carers working with children with complex health needs. York Sharing Care Scheme

Form 4 A useful summary of responsibilities in providing care. Hackney Family Back Up

Form 5 An example of a child health profile, used to gather detailed information about a child's health needs. Hackney Family Back Up

Form 6 A suggested format for developing a detailed health care plan. York Sharing Care Scheme

Form 7 The first of two detailed, but different, parental consent forms. Hackney Family Back Up

Form 8 A second parental consent form. Barnardo's Family Link in Newham

Form 9 An example of a training plan for a carer or sitter. Barnardo's Family Link in Newham

Forms 10 and 11 illustrate how different but acceptable, forms of language can be used in certifying training.

Form 10 A training record. Poole Shared Care Scheme

Form 11 A further training record. Barnardo's Family Link in Newham

Form 12 Record of medication form to be completed by parents. Poole Shared Care Scheme

Form 13 Medication sheet. Barnardo's Family Link in Newham

Form 14 Record of medication administered by project or non-parent carer.

Form 15 Record of medication.

Form 16 Review of competency form. Barnardo's Family Link in Newham

Included within this section are some examples of fact sheets and guidelines which relate to specific medical procedures. These are:

Form 17a A guide for parents and carers on home gastrostomy button feeding. Wiltshire Homeward

Form 17b Procedure for the administration of adrenaline using an Epipen. York Sharing Care Scheme

Form 17c Checklist for administering rectal diazepam.

Form 17d An information sheet on nasogastric feeding. Barnardo's Family Link in Newham

The dignity of risk

Form 1

York Sharing Care scheme

Background

The Sharing Care Additional Health Needs Scheme is operated in partnership with the York and Selby Primary Care Trust (PCT) and York Health Services Trust. The responsibilities of each of the partner agencies are as follows:

- **York and Selby Primary Care Trust** is responsible for funding the enhanced payments made to Sharing Carers who offer short breaks to children with additional health needs. At the beginning of each financial year the York and Selby PCT will indicate the level of funding available to City of York Council, and therefore the potential number of placements available to children with additional health needs.

  York and Selby PCT is responsible for commissioning a nurse co-ordinator and appropriate out-of-hours support for Sharing Carers who offer breaks to children with additional health needs, from the York Health Services Trust. The out-of-hours support involves open access by telephone or in person to the Paediatric Ward (Ward 17) at York District Hospital.

  The York and Selby PCT is responsible for informing all general practitioners about the Sharing Care Additional Health Needs Scheme, and making them aware of the potential implications for children requiring medical attention while in the Sharing Carer's home.

- **York Health Services Trust** is responsible for appointing an appropriately qualified person to the post of nurse co-ordinator for the Sharing Care scheme. That person will be a Registered Sick Children's Nurse (RSCN) with significant experience of working with disabled children who require nursing care.

  The York Health Services Trust will make arrangements for the out-of-hours support for carers. This will involve carers having telephone or personal access to the nursing staff on the paediatric ward.

  The York Health Services Trust will make arrangements for a nurse manager to offer regular clinical supervision to the nurse co-ordinator.

- **The City of York Community Services Department** is responsible for the day-to-day management of the Sharing Care scheme, and the recruitment, assessment and support of Sharing Carers, including those caring for children with additional health needs.

  The City of York is responsible for providing the funding for the standard care payment made to all Sharing Carers. Carers who offer short breaks to children with additional health needs also receive an enhanced allowance funded by the PCT and administered by the City of York.

  The City of York is responsible for providing office space, access to administrative services and staff supervision and annual appraisal to the nurse co-ordinator.

  The City of York is responsible for making arrangements for out-of-hours support to Sharing Carers, for any circumstances other than those concerning the health needs of the child.

Eligibility criteria

The Sharing Care scheme for children with additional health needs is available to children who require the administration of nursing procedures as a routine part of their daily living needs, or in emergency circumstances on a regular basis. For example, children who have any of the following needs would be deemed to have additional health needs, for the purposes of Sharing Care:

- have medication or nutrition administered through a medical appliance (for example, gastrostomy nasogastric tube or jejunostomy)
- are dependent on oxygen
- have a tracheotomy fitted
- have seizures that are poorly controlled
- have multiple allergies that are poorly controlled and regularly require the use of adrenaline injections.

There are also some children who have medical conditions requiring their Sharing Carers to be trained in certain procedures so that they are able to meet the child's emergency medical needs. However, where these procedures are not a regular part of the child's daily living, the child will not be deemed as having additional health needs for the purposes of Sharing Care, but they will still be able to access a service from the standard Sharing Care scheme.

Sharing Carers require training from the nurse co-ordinator for the following tasks, but for the purposes of Sharing Care they do not bring the child within the definition of having additional health needs:

- administering rectal medication (where seizures are well controlled, and the medication is rarely, if ever, administered)
- use of a nebuliser
- catheter care
- observation and care of a child who has a ventriculo-peritoneal shunt fitted
- observation and care of a child who has multiple allergies that are well managed, and has an Epipen prescribed but rarely, if ever, used
- carrying out suction of secretions from mouth/nose.

Nursing procedures that Sharing Care Additional Health Needs Carers can administer

Sharing Care Additional Health Needs Carers can be trained by the Sharing Care nurse co-ordinator and approved to carry out the following nursing procedures in their own homes:

- feeding, administering medication and care of a gastrostomy, nasogastric tube or jejunostomy
- administer oxygen
- manage a tracheostomy, including suction and emergency replacement of tube
- injections (intramuscular or subcutaneous) with a pre-assembled, pre-dose loaded syringe
- administration of rectal medication.

Procedures that Sharing Care Additional Health Needs Carers are prohibited from administering

As care is provided by Sharing Carers who are not necessarily qualified in nursing and it is provided in the Sharing Carer's own home, there may be some children whose needs are such that the scheme will be unable to accommodate them.

In line with advice from the Royal College of Nursing (in *Towards a Healthy Future*) and the Consultant Community Paediatrician in York, the following tasks cannot be carried out by Sharing Care Additional Health Needs Carers:

- giving injections involving assembling syringes, administering intravenously or administering controlled drugs
- programming of syringe drivers
- filling of oxygen cylinders
- passing a nasogastric tube
- any other nursing procedure deemed inappropriate by the Sharing Care co-ordinator or nurse co-ordinator.

Form 2

Craigavon and Banbridge Community Health and Social Service (CHSS) Trust

(This draft form was produced by Barnardo's and Craigavon and Banbridge CHSS Trust as part of their wrap-around project.)

Role and responsibilities of parents and guardians

Parents are the legal guardians of their child. They have parental responsibility and may, where appropriate, provide consent to treatment and care on behalf of their child. In promoting the ethos of partnership, parents should provide Trust staff with sufficient information about their child's medical condition, treatment and health care needs in order that a comprehensive assessment can be carried out. Subsequently, parents should discuss and negotiate with staff the caring arrangements which best suit and meet the child and family needs.

Where a non-parent carer is caring for the child
Parents and family members have a unique and special knowledge of their child and will be able to contribute significantly to the child's health and development. Parents should be encouraged to share health information on the child's needs with the non-parent carer.

- Prior written consent from the parents or guardian must be given before any medication or clinical/invasive procedure can be undertaken with the child.
- Procedures for the administration of any medication or clinical/invasive procedure should be drawn up in partnership with the child's parents or guardian. A clinical/invasive procedure will not be carried out by a staff member or non-parent carer without prior advice and/or training from an appropriate person.
- Parents should advise staff and/or the non-parent carer if there is a deterioration in a child's health.
- Should the non-parent carer note a deterioration in a child's health, he/she should inform the parents, Barnardo's manager or health care staff, where appropriate, as soon as possible.
- Trust/Barnardo's policy on the administration of medication and clinical/invasive procedures must be clear to all parents.
- Even very young children may be capable of consenting to a health care intervention or medical treatment. Parents, health care staff and non-parent carers should work together to help children communicate their opinions in relation to consent their care.

Role and responsibilities of Craigavon and Banbridge CHSS Trust

The Trust will promote a child- and family-centred approach to the care of the child with complex health care needs and her/his family. The Trust will work in partnership with the family to determine need and plan and co-ordinate effective provision within available resources. Resources issues may be addressed through a variety of channels – for example, Children's Services, planning sub-groups or the local Health and Social Service group. Arrangements will be made to ensure effective liaison between all members of the Trust's health and social care staff, and between Trust staff and Barnardo's.

Statement of agreement between Trusts and Barnardo's
A training policy will be agreed between Craigavon and Banbridge CHSS Trust and Barnardo's. It will be conditional on the Trust undertaking training of Barnardo's staff and their non-parent carers.

Training of a non-parent carer who is caring for the child

Craigavon and Banbridge CHSS Trust will provide appropriate advice and training for Barnardo's staff and their non-parent carers providing for a child's clinical needs.

- The Trust and Barnardo's will agree the specific clinical/invasive procedures which may be undertaken by Barnardo's staff and their non-parent carers.
- The Trust will design a training programme in respect of each area of training identified/agreed.
- Trust staff will implement the training programme in the identified areas and provide clinical supervision of the procedures as required.
- The Trust's trainer will advise Barnardo's as to whether the participant has reached the required level of competency in the given procedure by the end of the training programme.
- The Trust will provide update training in the selected areas as required.
- The Trust and Barnardo's will meet (bi)annually to review the needs of non-parent carers in undertaking clinical/invasive procedures.
- Barnardo's will advise parents as to the competency of non-parent carers to undertake a clinical/procedure.

Role and responsibilities of Barnardo's

Barnardo's, as an employer providing care on behalf of the Trust, will ensure that appropriate safety measures are in place to protect the employee under the Health and Safety at Work legislation. This will include ensuring that non-parent carers are appropriately trained and receive guidance on their responsibilities. Barnardo's will provide explicit reassurance that staff, non-parent carers and volunteers undertaking any form of clinical/invasive procedures are acting within the scope of their employment and abilities and that they are indemnified.

Barnardo's accepts responsibility, in principle, for staff or non-parent carers giving prescribed medicine to children or undertaking clinical/invasive procedures, subject to their adhering to the agreed standards of practice.

- Arrangements will be made to ensure effective liaison between Barnardo's and Craigavon and Banbridge CHSS Trust.
- Barnardo's staff and their non-parent carers will avail themselves of appropriate training provided by Craigavon and Banbridge CHSS Trust in the clinical/invasive care procedures required to meet a child specific needs.
- Barnardo's and the Trust will agree the specific clinical/invasive procedures which may be undertaken by Barnardo's staff and their non-parent carers.
- Barnardo's will advise the Trust of those staff requiring training in specific areas. Trust staff will implement the training programme in the identified areas and provide clinical supervision of the procedures as required.
- Barnardo's will arrange for their staff and non-parent carers to undertake training and supervision as required.
- Barnardo's will make staff available for update training as required.
- Barnardo's and the Trust will meet (bi)annually to review the needs of non-parent carers in undertaking clinical/invasive procedures.
- Barnardo's must ensure that, after their training, their staff member or non-parent carer is still willing to undertake the clinical/invasive procedure.
- Barnardo's will advise parents as to the competency of non-parent carers to undertake a clinical/procedure.

Role and responsibilities of the non-parent carer

- non-parent carer responsibility in relation to training/attendance, completion of course work, supervision
- update training

- working outside skills, knowledge
- advising Barnardo's manager if he/she does not wish to undertake clinical/invasive procedure despite undertaking training and being deemed competent by Trust
- reporting to parent, Barnardo's Manager, Trust staff, etc.

The non-parent carer acts as link worker for the family, liaising with various professionals who come into contact with the family, sharing relevant information with these colleagues, plan for special support for the family and the support worker. The non-parent carer also has responsibility for reviewing the child's and family's need for special support on a regular basis, the frequency of which is determined by the condition of the child.

Form 3

York Sharing Care scheme

This agreement should be completed with all Additional Health Needs Sharing Carers, in addition to the standard Sharing Carer Agreement. It makes clear what the Authority and Additional Health Needs Sharing Carers can expect of each other, over and above the standard agreement. This is not a legally binding document.

Support for Additional Health Needs Carers

You will have a link worker and will be entitled to all the support that standard Sharing Carers receive. In addition, you will receive support from the Sharing Care nurse co-ordinator in relation to the health needs of the children with additional needs that are linked to you. The nurse co-ordinator will contact you at least six-monthly, and you will also be able to make contact with them as necessary, for specific advice and support in respect of a nursing procedure.

Outside of normal office hours you will have access to the Emergency Duty Team in respect of all matters relating to the child's welfare except those relating to the health needs of the child.

You will have telephone and open access to the paediatric ward at York District Hospital for advice and support in relation to the nursing procedures needed by your link child. The paediatric ward will not give diagnoses or deal with emergencies. In the case of a medical emergency you should carry out the agreed protocol within the child's Individual Health Care Plan.

Training for Additional Health Needs Carers

As an Additional Health Needs Carer you will be required to undergo training from the nurse co-ordinator, for each nursing procedure that you are required to carry out, for each child. At the stage where a potential link has been identified with a child who has additional health needs, the nurse co-ordinator will work with you to identify an appropriate training programme to ensure that you are confident and competent about the nursing procedures needed to care for the child.

The nurse co-ordinator will issue you with a written copy of each nursing procedure, and will also complete a competency checklist for each nursing procedure. Within these there will be a section highlighting potential problems, and solutions.

You are required to co-operate with the training provided by the nurse co-ordinator, and to demonstrate that you are competent in carrying out each procedure. The nurse co-ordinator will complete a Record of Training for each nursing procedure that you are required to perform. The Record of Training also includes dates and details of refresher training. Refresher training in each nursing procedure will be provided at six-monthly intervals. You may request additional training or refresher training at any time, but are required to co-operate with the six-monthly refresher training.

The dignity of risk

Enhanced payments

As an acknowledgement of the additional training you are required to attend and the additional responsibility of managing a child's health needs, you will receive enhanced Sharing Care payments. The enhanced payment will be made for each time a child with additional health needs visits you, and is in addition to the standard Sharing Care allowance, which you will also receive.

Signed _____ Date _____

Additional Health Needs Carer _____

Agency decision-maker _____

Children with additional health needs – information for carers

Background

The Sharing Care Additional Health Needs Scheme began in December 1996 and is operated in partnership with the York and Selby Primary Care Trust (PCT) and York Health Services Trust.

The York Health Services Trust appoints a nurse co-ordinator who works closely with the Sharing Care Social Workers to support Sharing Carers who offer breaks to children with additional health needs. Out-of-hours support is also provided, which involves open access by telephone or in person, to the Paediatric Ward (Ward 17) at York District Hospital.

What does 'additional health needs' mean?

The Sharing Care scheme for children with additional health needs is available to children who require the administration of nursing procedures as a routine part of their daily living needs, or in emergency circumstances on a regular basis. For example, children who have any of the following needs would be deemed to have additional health needs, for the purposes of Sharing Care:
- have medication or nutrition administered through a medical appliance (for example gastrostomy, nasogastric tube or jejunostomy)
- are dependent on oxygen
- have a tracheotomy fitted
- have seizures that are poorly controlled
- have multiple allergies that are poorly controlled and regularly require the use of adrenaline injections.

Are all children with a medical condition classed as having 'additional health needs'?

No. There are also some children who have medical conditions requiring their Sharing Carers to receive training in certain procedures so that they are able to meet the child's emergency medical needs. However, where these procedures are not a regular part of the child's daily living, the child will not be deemed as having additional health needs for the purposes of Sharing Care, but they will still be able to access a service from the standard Sharing Care scheme.

Sharing Carers require training from the nurse co-ordinator for the following tasks, but for the purposes of Sharing Care they do not bring the child within the definition of having additional health needs:
- administering rectal medication (where the seizures are well controlled, and the medication is rarely, if ever administered)
- use of a nebuliser

Meeting children's health care needs

- catheter care
- observation and care of a child who has a ventriculo-peritoneal shunt fitted
- observation and care of a child who has multiple allergies that are well managed, and has an Epipen prescribed but rarely, if ever, used
- carrying out suction of secretions from mouth/nose.

What nursing procedures are Additional Health Needs Carers allowed to carry out?

Sharing Care Additional Health Needs Carers can be trained by the Sharing Care nurse co-ordinator and approved to carry out the following nursing procedures in their own homes:

- feeding, administering medication and care of a gastrostomy, nasogastric tube or jejunostomy
- administer oxygen
- management of a tracheotomy, including suction and emergency replacement of tube
- injections (intramuscular or subcutaneous) with a pre-assembled, pre-dose loaded syringe
- administration of rectal medication.

What nursing procedures are Additional Health Needs Carers NOT allowed to carry out?

As care is provided by Sharing Carers who are not necessarily nursing qualified and the care will be provided in the Sharing Carer's own home, there may be some children whose needs are such that the scheme will be unable to accommodate them.

In line with advice from the Royal College of Nursing (in Towards a Healthy Future) and the Consultant Community Paediatrician in York, the following tasks cannot be carried out by Sharing Care Additional Health Needs Carers:

- giving injections involving assembling syringes, administering intravenously, or controlled drugs
- programming of syringe drivers
- filling of oxygen cylinders
- passing a nasogastric tube
- any other nursing procedure deemed inappropriate by the Sharing Care co-ordinator and nurse co-ordinator.

How do I become an Additional Health Needs Carer?

Some people initially approach the Sharing Care scheme with a specific interest in caring for children with additional health needs. In this case they will be assessed within the same guidelines as all Sharing Carers, but with an additional assessment by the nurse co-ordinator and the Sharing Care Social Worker. The nurse co-ordinator assessment will address the carer's:

- ability to care for a disabled child who has additional health needs
- understanding of the nature of the tasks required
- ability to work alongside the nurse co-ordinator
- willingness to undertake extra training and updates of training.

The additional discussion areas covered by the Sharing Care Social Worker will include:

- any previous experience of working with, or caring for, children with additional health needs, whether in a professional, voluntary or family capacity
- their motivation for applying to become carers for children who have additional health needs
- their emotional capacity to undertake the care of a child who has additional health needs.

Following approval as Sharing Care Additional Health Needs Carers, the applicants are required to enter into the standard Sharing Carer written agreement with the Authority as well as a supplementary additional health needs written agreement.

Can I become an Additional Health Needs Carer if I am already a Sharing Carer?

Yes. Most of our Additional Health Needs Carers start as standard Sharing Carers and acquire an interest in caring for children with additional health needs through their involvement as Sharing Carers. You need to talk to your link worker if you are interested in becoming a Sharing Care Additional Health Needs Carer. In this situation the additional assessments are carried out as follows:

- the nurse co-ordinator visits you to assess (as above), and writes a brief report for Fostering/Sharing Care Panel
- your Sharing Care link worker visits you and covers the additional discussion areas, outlined above. Following this discussion, a brief report is prepared for the Fostering/Sharing Care Panel to consider a change in registration from Sharing Carer to Sharing Care Additional Health Needs Carer.

Following an extension to your approval you will be required to enter into an additional health needs written agreement.

What training will I receive?

You must not carry out any nursing procedures until you have received special training from the Sharing Care nurse co-ordinator. When a potential link with a child with additional health needs has been identified, the nurse co-ordinator will identify an appropriate training programme to ensure that you are competent and confident with all the nursing procedures needed to care for that child. This training will also involve the child's parents, to ensure continuity of care.

You will not be expected to undertake any nursing procedures with which you are uncomfortable. If there are any particular procedures that you do not feel able to manage, please discuss this with your link worker.

In carrying out a nursing procedure it is important to remember the child or young person's right to privacy and dignity.

The nurse co-ordinator will issue a written copy of each nursing procedure to you, and will also complete a competency checklist for each nursing procedure. Within these there will be a section highlighting potential problems, and solutions.

The nurse co-ordinator will complete a Record of Training for each nursing procedure that you perform. The Record of Training also includes dates and details of refresher training. Refresher training in any nursing procedure will be provided at six-monthly intervals and you will be required to co-operate with the refresher training. You may request additional training or refresher training at any time.

If there is any change to the nursing procedure or any additional procedures are necessary for the child, you must be shown again.

What support will I get as an Additional Health Needs Carer?

You will still have your identified Sharing Care link worker, but in addition the nurse co-ordinator will contact you on at least a six-monthly basis. You will also be able to make contact with the nurse co-ordinator during office hours, for specific advice and support in respect of a child's health needs.

Outside of normal office hours you will have access to the Emergency Duty Team in respect of concerns for all matters relating to the child's welfare, except those relating to the health needs of the child.

Additional Health Needs Carers have telephone and open access to the Paediatric Ward 17 at York District Hospital for advice and support in relation to the nursing procedures needed by the child. The Paediatric Ward will not deal with emergencies; these should go to the Accident and Emergency Department, as with all children.

How long will the introduction to a child take?

This depends entirely on how long you, the child's family and the child need to get to know each other and feel confident about the link.

Your Sharing Care link worker will give you written information about the child, on an Information for Prospective Carers form. In addition, the nurse co-ordinator will ensure that you are fully aware of the child's health needs and the implications for you in meeting these needs. You will also receive accurate information on the nursing procedures required.

After a series of introductory visits you, the child and their family will be invited to indicate whether you would like to proceed with the match. If so, a written placement agreement will be drawn up between yourselves, the child's family, and the Authority, before the child visits you alone. As part of the placement agreement, parents and children will be requested to give individual consent for each of the nursing procedures needed for the satisfactory care of their child.

What if something goes wrong?

Following on from the placement agreement meeting, the Sharing Care social worker, in conjunction with the child's social worker, will draw up a health care plan for the child. This individual health care plan will include what to do in an emergency according to the specific wishes of the child and their family, such as:

- the circumstances in which parents want to be contacted if their child is unwell
- who makes the decision about whether a child requires emergency medical attention
- who to contact if the parents are unavailable and the child requires admission to hospital
- which GP to contact if the child is unwell (that is, the child's GP or the carer's GP)
- who should transport the child to hospital if admission is required
- whether the family have any clear wishes about the child being resuscitated, or not
- in an emergency who is responsible for letting the health professionals know of any parental wishes regarding resuscitation
- who is responsible for providing the medication for the period of the short break, and checking it is in date
- anything else that is relevant to the child, their family situation, or the circumstances of the Additional Health Needs Carers.

You will receive a copy of each child's individual health care plan, and you will need to keep this in a safe place, where you can get it out easily in the case of an emergency. You will need to take the individual health care plan and the placement agreement with you if you seek emergency medical attention for the child, as these documents include the parents' signatures of consent.

Always let your Sharing Care link worker (or any of the Sharing Care workers) know about any emergency, as soon as possible after the event, and keep a record of it in your Sharing Care diary.

Am I covered by insurance?

As long as the correct nursing procedure is followed you will be covered in respect of any claim for personal injury/property damage that arises, subject to the terms, exceptions and limitations of the liability insurance policy.

What happens if the child's health needs change?

As part of the process of reviewing all Sharing Care links, the child's specific health needs will also be reviewed. The Sharing Care nurse co-ordinator will carry this out prior to a child's review to ensure that he/she continues to meet the criteria for the Sharing Care Additional Health Needs Scheme.

How much will I be paid to care for a child with additional health needs?

You will receive the standard Sharing Care allowance plus the additional health needs enhanced allowance, for each time a child with additional health needs visits you. The amount you receive will depend on how long the child's visit lasts.

Form 4

Hackney Family Back Up

	Task	Who is responsible
1	Profile and health assessment completed and updated annually	Parent with link worker
2	Health assessment signed	Child's GP
3	Informing carer and Hackney Family Back Up of changes in child health needs	Parent/s
4	Parent consent with placement agreement on file	Project administrator
5	Parent consent with placement agreement on file for new links	Link worker
6	Organising specific training and providing the carer with written information about the child's medical needs	Link worker
7	Specific consent for carrying out clinical procedures	Health trainer and parent/s
8	Provision of specific training	Health trainer
9	Recording the administration of medication	Short break carer
10	Reviewing and triggering update training	Link worker
11	Insurance	Project manager
12	Policy review annually	Management committee

The dignity of risk

Form 5

Hackney Family Back Up

Children Act 1989 – Arrangements for Placement of Children (General) Regulations 1991

Child's name _____ Date of birth _____

Parent/main carer's name _____

Address _____

_____

Telephone _____

GP's name _____

Surgery address _____

_____

Telephone _____

Hospital/clinics attended (eg Donald Winnicott Centre, Great Ormond Street) _____

_____

Consultant/relevant health professionals _____

Address _____

_____

Postcode _____ Telephone _____

Health questions

1   Epilepsy

    (a) Does your child have epilepsy or seizures? _____

    (b) What might cause a seizure (eg illness, flashing lights)? _____

    (c) What are the warning signs? _____

    (d) How often does your child have fits/seizures? _____

    (e) When your child has fits/seizures, what usually happens? _____

    (f) What should your carer do when your child has a fit. Please give precise instructions.

    _____

    (g) How long do the fits/seizures last for? _____

    (h) What does your child do after a fit, and what support do they need? _____

2   Does your child have any other specific medical needs/conditions? If yes, please give details.

    _____

3   Are your child's vaccinations up to date? Have there been any problems with vaccinations?

    _____

4   Has your child ever had an anti-tetanus injection? If so, when? _____

5   Does your child have sight or hearing difficulties? _____

6 Does your child wear glasses or hearing aid? If yes, please give details.

_____

7 Does your child have any problems with their teeth? If yes, please give details.

_____

8 Does your child have any special needs or problems with their eating (eg, do they have to have special food, are there certain foods they need to avoid, does food need to be presented in a certain way, do they use a nasogastric or gastrostomy tube)?

_____

_____

_____

_____

9 Does your child have any allergies? If yes, please give details.

_____

10 Does your child have any special needs or problems with their toileting (eg, do they need to use pads, are they prone to constipation or diarrhoea, is special help needed at certain times like menstruation)?

_____

_____

_____

_____

11 Does your child use any therapies (eg, speech, physiotherapy, patterning, etc)? If yes, please give details.

_____

12 Has your child had any serious illnesses or times in hospital? If yes, please give details.

_____

_____

_____

_____

13 If there is anything else we need to know about your child's health? If yes, please give details.

_____

_____

_____

_____

Please note: In addition to this written information, please discuss all your child's needs with your short break carer and the care co-ordinator at Hackney Family Back Up.

Completed by (family placement worker) _____

Parent/main carer _____ Signature of parent/main carer _____

Relationship to child _____ Date signed _____

Form 6

York Sharing Care scheme

This plan should be completed for each child who accesses a Sharing Care service and has additional health needs. These are guidelines for areas to cover in discussion, as each plan will need to be tailored to the individual circumstances.

Child's name _____ Date of birth _____

Address _____

_____

Child's family _____

Telephone _____ Mobile phone _____

Sharing carer/s _____ Telephone _____

Address _____

_____

Background Include a detailed description of the child's health needs, including a medical history summary, symptoms and likely consequences of no action being taken in the case of an emergency.

Outline of nursing procedure Give details about the nursing procedure that needs to be carried out, and who specifically is to be involved in doing it, under what conditions, when and how.

Training of Sharing Carers Who has been trained in the nursing procedure/s? What training has been given: what areas were covered in the training? When was the training given, and by whom? Date when training will be updated. Refresher training in administering the nursing procedure will be given at six-monthly intervals by the Sharing Care Nurse Co-ordinator. Have the Sharing Carers been trained in paediatric first aid and resuscitation? By whom, and when?

If the child is unwell while with the Sharing Carers In what circumstances do the parents want to be contacted if their child is unwell? Which GP should the Sharing Carers contact if the child is unwell – the child's GP or the Sharing Carer's GP? Who should the Sharing Carers contact if the parents are unavailable?

Example Below is a section from a child's health plan indicating what action should be taken when the child has an extreme allergic reaction.

Action	To be taken by
Remove from the possible source of the reaction	Sharing Carers
Give Piriton (antihistamine) liquid	Sharing Carers
Where appropriate assist to use his or her inhaler	Sharing Carers
At the onset of any reaction, Sharing Carers will contact the parents or their appointed nominees if they feel it is appropriate or want to contact them	Sharing Carers

However, in the event of a whole-body reaction or severe asthma attack, emergency procedures would be followed.

Form 7

Hackney Family Back Up

As a parent using Hackney Family Back Up (HFBU) there are several things you need to know and understand:

1   You retain full parental rights and responsibilities.

2   The short break carer or link worker has a duty to inform you about any accident, illness or injury that happens to your child as soon as possible.

3   It is your responsibility to give the short break carer and HFBU full details of your child's medication prior to care taking place, and to update the carer and HFBU whenever there are any changes. By signing this consent form you give permission for the short break carer to administer this medication on your behalf. HFBU cannot be held responsible for information regarding medication that is inaccurate.

4   By signing this document, you give consent for HFBU to contact your child's GP or other health professional for verification of medical information, and for the GP to give any further information relevant to your child in respect of their short break care.

5   Whilst we would do our best to contact you first, by signing this document you give permission for the carer to seek medical treatment and any emergency treatment required by your child to be carried out which could include emergency operative treatment, including the administration of anaesthetic if authorised by a medical practitioner.

6   The Placement Agreement between parents and HFBU specifies the project's requirements as regards the short break carer who will care for your child. Please read it carefully and make sure you understand it so that you are able to sign the following statement.

I agree to my child _____ being cared for under the terms and conditions specified above.

Signed _____

Dated _____

Relationship to child _____

Please note: Carers are only authorised to administer prescribed oral medication. If your child requires a clinical procedure (eg rectal medication, nasogastric or gastrostomy care, stoma care) or therapies (eg physiotherapy), the carer cannot undertake these until HFBU has been notified, the carer has been trained, and a separate consent form has been signed.

Form 8

Barnardo's Family Link in Newham

Parental consent for carer or sitter to administer medication or carry out a clinical procedure

The Project's carer and/or sitter will not give your child medicine or carry out invasive clinical procedure unless you complete and sign this form, and the project leader has agreed that the carer and/or sitter can do so.

Details of child

Name _____ Date of birth _____

Address _____

_____

Condition or illness _____

Clinical procedure, eg tube feeding

Type of procedure _____

Method _____

Timing _____

Parental consent

Delete the statements that do not apply

- I consent to my child's carer/sitter administering prescribed medication in accordance with the attached Medication Sheet.
- I consent to my child's carer/sitter administering prescribed medication, not described on my child's medication sheet, for short-term illnesses, eg antibiotics or other prescribed medicines.
- I consent to my child's carer/sitter giving my child _____ mls of paracetamol as necessary, when required.
- I consent to the carer/sitter carrying out my child's therapies, eg physiotherapy.

Name _____ Relationship to child _____

Address _____

_____

Signature _____ Date _____

Child's consent

I consent to my carer/sitter administering my prescribed medication and/or carrying out the above clinical procedure.

Signature _____ Date _____

Any other information that the carer/sitter should know which is not covered on this form, eg how the child communicates, how the child indicates discomfort.

Form 9

Barnardo's Family Link in Newham

Clinical procedures and therapies consent and training form

Carer's name _____

This training plan relates to (child's name) _____

Description of procedure/therapy

How long will the child need this to be undertaken (please state if not known) _____

Type of training received _____

Procedures to take in an emergency _____

Date training completed _____ Training provided by _____

Name _____

Profession and title _____

I confirm that _____ (carer's name) has
received the training detailed above and is competent to carry out the necessary
clinical procedure or therapy.

I recommend this training is updated (please state how often) _____

Trainer's signature _____

Training received by (name) _____ Date _____

I confirm that I have received the training above, understand the clinical procedure or
therapy and feel confident to carry it out.

Carer's signature _____

The above training will be reviewed each time the child's profile and health
assessment records are updated.

The dignity of risk

Form 10

Poole Shared Care Scheme

Specialised needs form

A *For completion by a community paediatric nurse*

Child's name _____ Date of birth _____

I confirm that the person(s) named as follows _____ has/have
been trained by _____ to undertake the following
tasks. (Give details of procedures, times or situations in which they are needed and
nature of training given attach additional pages if necessary.)

_____

_____

Signed _____ Date _____

Designation _____

Address _____

_____

B *For completion by a general practitioner in the primary health care team
with whom the child is registered*

I agree that the above procedures and training are appropriate to the needs of the
above child

Signed _____ Date _____

Designation _____

Address _____

_____

Each signatory please return completed form to _____
Shared Care

Original to be kept on child's file, copies to parents, shared carer and shared carer's file.

Form 11

Barnardo's Family Link in Newham

Carer's/sitter's training record: carrying out of clinical procedures

Name of carer or sitter _____

Name of child for whom training has been received _____

Type of training received (including details of the clinical procedure) _____
_____

Date training completed _____ Training provided by _____

Name _____

Profession and title _____

I confirm that _____ has received the training detailed above
and is competent to carry out the necessary clinical procedure.

Trainer's signature _____ Date _____

Training received by _____

I confirm that I have received the training detailed above.

Staff/carer's signature _____ Date _____

Agreed review date _____

The dignity of risk

Form 12

Poole Shared Care Scheme

Child's name _____ Date of birth _____

1   As a parent of the above named child, I confirm that he/she requires the
following medication.

Medication	Time given	Amount	How given

2   I give permission for the person(s) named below to hold the medicines and
assist/supervise my child to take them as detailed above.

_____

3   I undertake to notify the carers in writing of any changes in medication.

4   I give permission for the above-named child to be given the following
non-prescribed painkiller/temperature reducer if appropriate.

_____

5   In giving this permission I accept full responsibility for my child's welfare.

Signed _____ Date _____

Relationship _____

Address _____

_____

For completion by the carer

1   I agree to hold the medication and assist/supervise the above-named child to
take them as detailed above.

2   I agree to keep a written record of medication given.

Signed _____ Date _____

Address _____

_____

Original to be kept on child's file, copies to parent, short break carer, short break
carer's file.

Form 13

Barnardo's Family Link in Newham

It is important to list all medication, however it is taken.

Child's name _____   Time _____

Name of medication _____   Dosage _____

How medication is given _____

Why medication is given _____

_____

_____

_____

NB Any changes to the above medication, ie dosage or timing, must be confirmed in writing by a qualified medical practitioner before the next short term break

Guidance for completing medication sheet

- Ask the parent to produce the medicines for you to look at so that you can copy the names of the medicines on to the sheet.
- Check that the appropriate child's name is on the bottle and that the medication is within the expiry date. (NB Antibiotics in liquid form only keep for 7–10 days once made up.)
- Note the dosage, time the medication should be given, how it is given and why it is given (eg for asthma, for epilepsy, etc).
- Note down alternative medicines or therapies, eg homeopathic medicine that the child has regularly.
- Draw parent's attention to the statement on the bottom of the sheet re changes to medication.

The dignity of risk

Form 14
Record of medication administered by project or non-parent carer

Date _____

Child's name _____ Time _____

Name of medication and method of administration _____

Dose given _____

Any reaction _____

Signature of staff or carer _____

Print name _____

Record of administration of rectal diazepam

To be completed when rectal diazepam (Stesolid) has been administered.

Patient's name _____ Patient's number _____

Address _____

Date of birth _____

GP _____

Date of administration _____ Time of administration _____

Given by (signature) _____

Record of events preceding the administration of rectal diazepam (Stesolid)

Type of seizure _____ Number of seizures _____

How long did seizure last? _____ Frequency of seizure _____

Records of events following the administration of rectal diazepam (Stesolid)

Length of recovery _____

Action taken in accordance with protocol _____

Signature _____ Name (block capitals) _____

Date/time _____

One copy for patient's records, one copy to accompany patient if admitted to hospital.

Form 15
Record of medication

Medication administered to (name of child) _____

Date	Name of medicine	Dose	Time given	Comments (eg, given late, child did not want to take it, any reactions or side effects, etc	Carer's signature

The dignity of risk

Form 16
Review of carers/sitters training on administration of clinical procedures

Barnardo's Family Link in Newham

Name of carer or sitter _____

Name of child for whom training has been received _____

Type of training received (including details of the clinical procedure) _____

_____

_____

_____

_____

Date training completed _____

Training provided by _____

Name _____

Profession and title _____

I confirm that _____ continues to be competent in carrying out the necessary clinical procedure.

Trainer's signature _____ Date _____

Comments _____

_____

_____

_____

Form 17a
A guide for parents and carers:
home gastrostomy button feeding

Wiltshire Homeward

Gastrostomy feeding has been suggested for your child to improve their nutritional status and growth. It also enables you to give medicines and fluids. The gastrostomy tube or button goes through the skin directly into their stomach.

Although your child will receive a feed through their tube, they should be able to eat and drink as usual with a gastrostomy tube or button in place. Involving your child to join in at family mealtimes is important. It gives them an opportunity to experience food. Encourage your child to touch and taste, just like everyone else, even if it makes a mess.

In babies, using a dummy will help to stimulate their lips, gums, cheeks and lips. It will also help to encourage them to try food.

The purpose of this booklet is to help us work through the information together. There are many dolls, colouring books and stories to help your child understand about gastrostomy feeding.

The children's community nurse and dietician will follow your child's progress and can visit you at home to offer practical advice and support.

Contact numbers

Community children's nurse _____

Dietician _____

Hospital ward _____

Supplies of feed and equipment by Homeward

On discharge your child will be supplied with 7 days' supply of feed and the necessary equipment required for feeding at home. Further deliveries of feed and equipment will be made by a clinical support service called Homeward.

The dietician will contact your GP requesting monthly prescriptions for feed. You can collect the prescription yourself and send it to Homeward in the envelope provided as soon as possible. Alternatively, you can request Homeward to contact your GP directly, to obtain the prescription on your behalf. You will need to sign a consent form to allow this to happen.

Providing Homeward receive a prescription, further supplies of feed and equipment will be delivered to your home within the next 7 days at a pre-arranged time.

Homeward delivery system
Homeward will deliver all your child's feeding equipment every month as long as needed. With the first delivery you will receive an information pack. This will include a list of delivery dates and a product checklist.

Prior to each delivery, Homeward will contact you to do a stocktake to ensure the appropriate supplies are sent. Further details are available about the system as required.

Homeward provides an advice and replacement service for their pumps. If you have problems with your feeding pump initially refer to the trouble-shooting guide in the

The dignity of risk

pump handbook. However, if you are unable to make the pump work properly, contact Homeward, who will aim to send a replacement in 24 hours. The faulty pump will be collected at the next delivery. Your pump should be serviced by Homeward annually.

Holidays

If you are planning a holiday, ring Homeward, who will be able to help and advise you on the transport of your feed and equipment.

Your child's daily feeding plan

If your child enjoys food and drinks and there is no problem with their swallow, they should continue to eat and drink with the feeding tube in place. Your dietician will advise you on the type and volume of feed to give. Part or all of your child's nutrition can be given down the tube depending on how much food and fluids they are able to manage themselves. Their intake may vary from day to day, so you should use the following as a guide.

Details of feed _____

_____

Feeding plan _____

_____

Quantity to aim for in 24 hours _____

_____

Equipment for feeding

The table below shows the equipment that you will need for feeding your child at home, and where it will be supplied from.

Equipment	Description	Manufacture and order code	Quantity per month	How supplied
Feeding tube				
Extension sets				
Giving set				
Reservoir				
Pump				
Syringes				
Other, eg litmus				

Keeping feeds safe to use

To help keep your child free from any upset tummy or diarrhoea, when preparing to give a feed always:
- wash and dry hands thoroughly
- wash working surfaces to be used with hot soapy water
- prepare feed away from other foods.

Storage of feeds

Store all feeds in a cool dry place, avoiding direct sunlight and heat. Check expiry dates prior to use.

Once a bottle of feed is opened, or powdered feed prepared, keep refrigerated in a sealed or covered container and use within 24 hours.

Meeting children's health care needs

The required quantity of milk can be taken out of the refrigerator about 30 minutes before the feed is due, to allow the milk to warm to room temperature.

Alternatively, the required amount of feed can be warmed before giving, to make it more comfortable for your child, but you should throw away any unused feed. Avoid warming up the feed again.

Ready-to-use feeds
These feeds are heat treated and therefore can be stored unopened at room temperature for several months.

Powdered feeds
When using powdered feeds, use the contents within one month of opening.

Use cooled boiled water or sterile water to make up the feeds. Cooled boiled water can be stored in a clean lidded container for up to 24 hours, and then the unused water should be thrown away. Bottles of sterile water are single-use only, so once a bottle of sterile water has been opened, any water left over should be thrown away.

Extra care is needed when making up a feed to keep it as clean as possible.

Giving your child a bolus feed through a gastrostomy button

A bolus feed means giving a set amount of feed over a short time, usually 20–30 minutes. The feed is poured into a syringe and allowed to run through the gastrostomy button by gravity. The advantage of bolus feeding is that it fills your child's stomach and then leaves it to empty as normally happens when eating meals. Your nurse will help you until you feel confident.

You will need:
- feeding syringe – without the plunger
- feed
- water for flushing
- extension set.

How to give a bolus feed
- Clean any work surface you are going to use with hot soapy water.
- Wash and dry your hands.
- Prepare the feed – remember to check the expiry date.
- When ready to give the feed settle your child comfortably, seat in as upright position as is possible.
- Attach the feeding syringe to the gastrostomy extension set.
- Connect the extension set to the gastrostomy button, matching the black mark, then turning in the direction of the arrow.
- Close the clamp on the extension set as near to the button as possible.
- Pour _____ ml water into the syringe, open the clamp and let the water run through, then close the clamp.
- Pour feed into the syringe. Let the feed run through into the extension set, allowing any air from the tubing to bubble up. Open the clamp, let the feed run through, topping up the syringe with feed as necessary.
- Do not allow the syringe to empty until the required amount of feed is given.
- The feed should run through with gravity and not need pushing through.
- You can alter the rate by raising the syringe to run the feed in quicker or lowering the syringe to slow or stop the feed.
- Run the feed through at the speed which is comfortable for your child. This is variable but usually takes between 10 and 30 minutes.
- At the end of the feed, close the clamp. Run _____ ml water into the syringe, let the air bubble up from the tubing, then open the clamp and let the water run through to flush the gastrostomy button.

The dignity of risk

- Disconnect the extension set and close the gastrostomy button.
- Try to keep your child in an upright position for about 30 minutes afterwards.
- Wash the extension tube and syringes in hot soapy water, rinse well and air dry then store dry in a closed container ready for next feed.

Giving your child a feed through a gastrostomy button using a pump

Using a pump will enable the feed to be given more slowly, which will improve your child's tolerance of the feed. The nurse or dietician will show you how to set up the pump.

You will need:
- feed and container or pack of feed
- feeding pump
- giving set
- extension set
- water in syringe for flushing.

How to give a continuous feed
- Clean any work surface you are going to use with hot soapy water.
- Wash and dry your hands.
- Connect giving set to the pack of feed using a non-touch technique, and run the feed through the giving set as shown. This is known as priming the giving set.
- Insert the giving set into the pump. Further information is in the pump handbook if needed.
- When you are ready to start the feed, settle your child comfortably, as upright as possible. If feeding overnight, slightly elevate the top of the bed by puffing a pillow under the mattress. Alternatively, support their upper body with pillows, trying to avoid your child from lying completely flat.
- Connect the extension set to the gastrostomy button, matching the black marks then turning in the direction of the arrow.
- Close the clamp on the extension set as near to the button as possible.
- Pour _____ ml water into the syringe, open the clamp and let the water run through. Close the clamp and take the syringe off.
- Remove the cap off the end of the primed giving set before attaching it to the extension set. Remember to keep the end cap of the giving set if you will be using the feeding system again within 24 hours. Open the clamp on the giving set and extension set.
- Make sure the pump is set at the correct rate and switch the pump on.
- It is worth tightening all the connections on the giving set before feeding, to prevent feed leaking from any loose connections.
- If the pump alarms refer to the pump trouble-shooting guide. You may want to speak a nurse or dietician if the problem persists.

Advice on keeping feed and feeding equipment safe to use

If using a pack system If using more than one pack of feed always keep the empty pack connected to the giving set until you need to attach the new pack. This prevents the giving set being left open to the air and will reduce the risk of introducing germs into the system. Do not wash or flush the giving set before connecting the new pack. Use a new giving set every 24 hours.

If using a ready-to-use feed in feed containers Pour in enough feed for up to 12 hours so that you only need to top up the container once more in the 24 hours. This will reduce the risk of introducing germs into the system. Do not wash or flush the giving set and container when tipping up. Use a new container and giving set every 24 hours.

If using powder feeds or decanting ready-to-use feeds into a container The dietician or community children's nurse will advise you on quantities to use at one time and how often to change the feeding system.

At the end of the feed

You will need a syringe containing water for flushing. When the required volume of feed has been given:
- switch the pump off and clamp the giving set and extension set
- wash and dry your hands
- disconnect the giving set from the extension set. Replace the cap onto the end of the giving set if using again to prevent leaving the feed exposed to air
- flush the gastrostomy button with water as previously, then remove the extension set and close the button
- wash the syringe and extension set in hot soapy water, rinse well and air dry then store dry in a closed container ready for the next feed.

Keeping equipment safe to use

The following information concerns the use and re-use of equipment for gastrostomy feeding. This applies to the following equipment:
- syringes and extension sets
- feeding containers and giving sets if using a delivery system.

The advice we give is
- Use a new giving set and feed container every 24 hours.
- Use a new syringe every 24 hours.
- Use a new gastrostomy extension set once a week.

Care of equipment

Syringes and gastrostomy extension sets must be cleaned every time they have been used, if they are going to be used again within the recommended period.
- Separate the barrel and plunger of the syringe and rinse the equipment well in clean water.
- Wash syringes and extension sets thoroughly with hot water and detergent.
- Rinse again and dry excess water with a disposable paper towel (do not use a cloth towel).
- Allow to dry in air.
- Store the dried pieces separately in a clean environment.
- For infants under 12 months, all extension sets and syringes used should be sterilised.

The nurse or dietician will discuss your child's individual needs with you. We appreciate that requirements for equipment may change, so please do not hesitate to contact the nurse or dietician if you feel the quantity of supplies has become inappropriate. Further supplies will be available from the community children's nurse or Homeward.

Care of your gastrostomy button

The gastrostomy button is a device to help give feed, fluid and/or medicine to your child. It is specially measured for your child. The button lies flat against the tummy wall and is held in position by a water-filled balloon. There is an anti-reflux valve in the button, preventing leakage of stomach contents through the button.

The dignity of risk

Daily care

It is important to keep the skin under the button as clean and dry as possible. Cotton buds are useful for cleaning the skin area around the button.

The button should be turned in a full circle once a day.

Dressings should not be required, as these may make the skin moist.

Flushing the gastrostomy button

Always flush the button with water before and after giving medicines and feeds. Use fresh tap water for flushing, unless your child is under six months in which case use cooled boiled water. Do not use bottled or filtered water.

To check for leakage from the balloon of the button

Every week check that you still have adequate water in the balloon of the button. To do this, remove the water from the balloon with a 5 ml syringe. At this point, do not remove the tube, but check that 5 ml of water was removed. Re-inflate the button with a full 5 ml of water or full amount advised, and inform the nurse if less than 5 ml of water was removed.

If on a weekly check you find the fluid is less than usual, re-inflate with the full amount of water required. Recheck the fluid the following day and if you are still losing fluid from the balloon, this would indicate that a new button is required. A button tends to last three to four months on average.

Stoma problems

Contact your hospital for advice if:

* the stoma is persistently red or bleeds
* the stoma gives off a smell
* the skin around the stoma is swollen and red
* there is pus around the stoma.

Commonly asked questions

What should I do if the gastrostomy is coming out?

Check that the balloon is still inflated. Reinflate with 5 ml of water if possible. If the balloon has burst it is important that the button is replaced as soon as possible. If you have been provided with a spare button and have been shown how to do this, then you may replace the button. If not, you should tape the button in place and visit your local hospital.

What should I do if the tube gets blocked?

Try flushing with water. If the tube still remains blocked, contact your community children's nurse or ward. To prevent the tube blocking in the future, always flush the tube after any feed or medicines.

Can I give medicines down the tube?

All liquid medicines can be given through the button. If you are given any medicines as tablets, ask your chemist if a liquid form is available. Alternatively, ask the chemist if the medicines can be finely crushed and mixed thoroughly with water to give down the tube.

Should my child still brush their teeth?
Even though your child might not be eating or drinking, they should continue brushing their teeth to promote good dental care. If you have any concerns or questions about mouth care ask your community children's nurse for advice.

Remember: if you are ever in doubt or unsure about any aspect of your child's care, please do not hesitate to call and speak to a nurse, doctor or dietician. Everyone here is more than happy to help your family.

The dignity of risk

Form 17b
procedure for the administration of adrenaline using an Epipen

York Sharing Care Scheme

Adrenaline is given in an emergency to children and adults who are experiencing anaphylaxis as a result of a reaction to a particular allergen.

Allergic reactions/anaphylactic shock

These can present the person with a sense of impending doom, anxiety, headache, flushed face, feeling warm, swelling of the mouth, lips, eyes and/or whole face, rash, drooling from the mouth, noisy breathing, difficulty in breathing, rhinitis, wheezy cough, abdominal pain, vomiting, diarrhoea, loss of consciousness, seizures, low blood pressure, hypovolaemic shock, respiratory and cardiac arrest, or death.

Adrenaline

This is a hormone naturally secreted from the adrenal gland. The action of this hormone is similar to that of normal stimulation of the sympathetic nervous system. For example, adrenaline:
- dilates the bronchioles in the lungs
- raises blood pressure by constricting surface vessels and thus stimulates cardiac output
- releases glycogen from the liver.

Purpose of giving adrenaline via the Epipen

As a holding measure to slow down the allergic reaction an Epipen only administers a small amount of adrenaline. If after 10–15 minutes the person is not showing some signs of recovery a second Epipen can be administered (according to specific instructions for the individual). This is an emergency situation – ring for an ambulance and ask for a paramedic team.

Sharing Carers must:
- always have a contact telephone number for the child/young person's family
- have full information on the person being cared for – ie, allergens responsible for allergic reaction and what sort of reaction to expect. Usually antihistamine medication is given orally before progressing on to using the Epipen
- have written permission from the parent to administer the Epipen if anaphylaxis occurs.

Equipment

Two Epipens should be readily available at all times, ie, one or two with the person and one in a medicine cupboard or with the carer.

Epipens should be stored at room temperature and must not be stored in a refrigerator (see individual health care plan for details of the specific individual).

Check weekly that Epipens are in date. Check at the same time that the adrenaline is clear in colour – it should not be brown. This can be seen through the viewing window on the Epipen. Adrenaline changes colour when exposed to extreme heat or sunlight.

In the event of anaphylaxis

Be aware of the first signs of allergic reaction in the person (refer to individual health care plan). Ensure that two Epipens are available. You may need to remove the child to another room.

While you are sitting the child on an upright chair instruct someone else to ring for an ambulance and contact the family. Explain to ambulance control what is wrong with the person and that you need a paramedic team, as they have oxygen, suction, airways and expertise. If you are the only carer, give the Epipen before contacting the emergency services and parents.

Explain to the child what you are going to do, ie, give them an injection of adrenaline using the Epipen. If the child is wearing trousers it is advisable to remove them before using the Epipen. However, in an absolute emergency you can inject through the trousers into the leg.
- Take the grey end off the pen (instructions are on the side of the pen)
- Locate the area to be injected (into the muscle of the upper leg, mid-line outer thigh.
- Hold the pen as you would hold a dagger, at right angles to the leg.
- Press the black end of the pen firmly into the leg muscle (this is painful) until it clicks and hold in place for 10 seconds (count to 10).
- Remove the needle and gently massage the leg.
- Put the used Epipen out of reach of other people as the needle protrudes significantly, ie into a plastic container.

If the child has not shown any signs of recovery after 10 seconds, the Epipen can be used on the other leg (see individual health care plan for further details). Repeat the instructions above.

Stay with the child at all times and reassure them.

Competency checklist for the administration of adrenaline using an Epipen

Child's name _____   Sharing Carer's name _____

Aims
- To teach Sharing Carers about the signs and symptoms of an allergic reaction to a particular allergen or allergens.
- To teach Sharing Carers how and where to safely administer adrenaline using an Epipen.

Objectives
- To fully inform the carer about the child's condition, ie exactly what she/he is allergic to, how does she/he initially present, at what stage does the Epipen have to be administered (see individual health care plan).
- To show the carer the placebo Epipen and use this as a demonstration model.
- To show the carer the video which gives explanation about allergic reactions and how to administer the Epipen.
- To teach the carer the procedure to be followed if the Epipen needs to be given. Explain that full instructions are written on the side of the pen.
- To ensure that carers are aware that the Epipen must not be stored in a refrigerator, as it needs to be stored at 25 degrees centigrade (that is, room temperature).
- Ensure that Sharing Carers are aware that if adrenaline is exposed to extreme heat or sunlight this medication turns brown. Therefore the Epipen should be checked regularly to ensure that the medication is clear, this can be viewed through the viewing window. Check the expiry date on the pen on a weekly basis.

- Ensure that Sharing Carers are informed as to whether they can administer a second Epipen if the child is showing no signs of recovery. Carers must be informed about the length of time they should wait before administering a second Epipen (usually 10–15 minutes).
- The Sharing Carer must be informed that this is a paediatric emergency and that the emergency services must be contacted straight after administration of the Epipen if you are alone. Where possible send a second person to ring for the ambulance while you are administering the Epipen. Inform the carer that this is just a holding measure and that the child will need to go to hospital.
- The Sharing Carer must be informed that a contact telephone number for the parent must be available at all times.
- The Sharing Carer must stay with the child at all times and give reassurance.
- The Sharing Carer will be given written information about allergy, anaphylaxis and the procedure for administering the Epipen. They must agree to read this following the teaching session.
- The Sharing Carer will have all information given in a clear, concise way and terminology will be explained.

Comments specific to the individual

- Can two Epipens be used? _____
- When should a second Epipen be given? _____
- Are there any special instructions? _____
_____

Nurse demonstration

Signature _____ Date _____

Carer demonstration

Signature _____ Date _____

Form 17c
Checklist for administering rectal diazepam

1 Refer to protocol checklist.

2 Collect equipment:
   - gloves
   - lubricant
   - tube of diazepam
   - disposal bag

3 Turn child on to left side

4 Put on gloves

5 Lubricate nozzle

6 Remove tube cap

7 Insert nozzle into anus.
   - Aged over 3 years – full length or nozzle
   - Aged under 3 – half length of nozzle

8 Empty contents of tube into anus by squeezing tube firmly between index finger and thumb.

9 When tube is empty withdraw and discard into the disposal bag.

10 Maintain the child's position for a few seconds holding the buttocks together to prevent seepage.

11 Remove gloves and place in disposal bag.

12 Wash hands and make child comfortable.

13 The administration of rectal diazepam is an emergency procedure, but the child's privacy and dignity must be kept at all times.

14 Make a record of the time of administration of rectal diazepam.

15 Record all observations made after the treatment has been carried out.

The dignity of risk

Form 17d
An information sheet on nasogastric feeding

Barnardo's Family Link in Newham

Nasogastric feeding is a means of providing food via a tube passed through the nostril past the opening to the lungs (pharynx), and into the stomach. This is a safe method of feeding if you ensure that the tube is still in the stomach immediately before feeding. Always check the tube is in the stomach by drawing back fluid from the tube with a syringe (2 ml or 5 ml) and testing it with blue litmus paper to see that it turns pink. A pink reaction will confirm position in the stomach.

Equipment
- kangaroo feeding set or large syringe
- 2 ml or 5 ml syringe
- feed
- cooled, boiled water
- litmus paper

If fluid cannot be drawn back, try repositioning the child. For example, lie the child flat or on her/his side. If this still does produce fluid do not attempt to use the tube for feeding. Phone the child's parents and inform them that a feed cannot be given. The parents may want to come and test the tube themselves, or if the Community Children's Nursing Team is available they can be called to see if they can visit and test the tube.

If the tube is in the stomach and the litmus paper test is passed then the warmed prepared feed can be given via an administration set. This is normally a kangaroo set. Small babies sometimes use a 20 ml syringe. This allows the feed to be given slowly and safely.

The kangaroo set should be put together and primed with feed before being attached to the feeding tube. This is to prevent air being introduced to the child's stomach.

The feed should be given slowly to prevent vomiting.

Once the feed is finished the tube should be flushed with clean water to prevent the tube becoming blocked with dried milk feed.

If you are in any doubt about where the tube is or that the feed is going into the lungs, stop the feed and call for medical help immediately. If the tube is in the lungs the child will cough continuously, choke and go blue. Gently remove the tape by the nose and slowly pull out the tube.

④ Moving and handling

This chapter covers
The legislative framework
Survey of moving and handling issues
The East Sussex judgment
Policy guidance: what needs to be in place?
Conclusion
References
**Checklist of key points: moving and
    handling**
Appendix: The law in detail
Sample forms and guidance

The legislative framework

The Manual Handling Operations
Regulations 1992 require employers to assess
the risk in relation to manual handling,
avoid manual handling operations which
involve a risk of injury if possible, mechanise
handling where possible, and, in all cases,
reduce risk to what is 'reasonably
practicable'. These regulations were written
under the Health and Safety at Work Act
1974 and their purpose was to implement
the European Directive. They were part of a
wider campaign to reduce back injuries.
Between 1992 and 1995 there were 14,000
manual handling accidents reported to the
Health and Safety Executive (HSE), 60 per
cent of which involved moving people.

'Reasonably practicable' is defined in the
Regulations as:

> 'An employee has satisfied his/her duty if
> s/he can show that any further
> preventative steps would be grossly
> disproportionate to the further benefit that
> would accrue from their introduction.'

It is important to remember that the
Manual Handling Operations Regulations do
not prohibit manual handling, but rather
create a hierarchy of measures for reducing
the risks involved in manual handling.

When the Manual Handling Operations
Regulations came into force, they appeared
to have minimal impact on services, but
whether this was through ignorance or
interpretation is difficult to tell.
Implementation concerns became more clear
as case law developed, and the Royal College
of Nursing/National Back Pain Association
guidance (1997) was used as a reference. In
1997 it was agreed in court (*Edwards vs
Waltham Forest*) that this document was
'standing as agreed practical guidance
(which) means that it may be referred to by
the court'. This had huge implications for
services, as the document concentrated
almost exclusively on people in hospital
settings rather than on those with care needs
in the community.

Sue Cunningham (*Disability, Oppression and
Public Policy,* 2000) also points out that the
stricter interpretation of the regulations also
related to the loss of Crown immunity by the
NHS. In 1998 Crown immunity from
prosecution for non-compliance with health
and safety legislation was largely withdrawn,
and from 1998 to 2001 there were 34
successful prosecutions by the HSE against
NHS employers. Civil actions are also on the
increase, with an average award for manual
handling injuries of about £60,000; one of
the larger awards to date is £450,000. Within
one of the large children's charities, concerns
were further heightened when compensation
payments reached £500,000. While the
payments were covered by insurance, the
charity was concerned that escalating
insurance costs could lead to less money
available for direct service provision.

The law relating to lifting and handling
has two principal objectives: accident
prevention and compensation to the injured
lifter.

The main pieces of legislation are:
- The Health and Safety at Work Act 1974
- The Management of Health and Safety at

Work Regulations 1992
- Manual Handling Operations 1992
- Provision and Use of Work Equipment Regulations 1988 (PUWER)
- Lifting Operations and Lifting Equipment Regulations 1988 (LOLER).

Details of these Acts and Regulations are in Appendix 1 at the end of this chapter.

Survey of moving and handling issues

In July 2003, questionnaires were sent to 195 schemes on the Shared Care Network database requesting information on moving and handling. Sixty per cent (116) of schemes responded. A similar study (Jones and Lenehan 2000) had been carried out two years earlier. This produced the alarming findings that 46% of schemes were suspending existing placements and 69% were unable to provide new placements because of the impact of the regulations. This meant that the very children that the schemes had been set up to provide services for were being denied access to those services. As a result, Shared Care Network, Barnardo's and the Council for Disabled Children lobbied to raise the issue within the Department of Health and asked them to provide schemes with advice and information.

Findings of the latest survey (in July 2003) show some improvement, but it is difficult to tell whether this is because schemes are better able to access information and support or because children with moving and handling needs are not being referred to schemes.

Key findings of the July 2003 (Carlin 2003) survey show that:
- Ninety-one per cent of short break schemes surveyed have diversified and provide more than one type of service.
- The majority of schemes (69%) did not operate a no-lift policy.
- Less than half the schemes surveyed (44%) had a written moving and handling policy.
- General advice on moving and handling and specific advice on individual

placements was received by staff working in nearly 90% of the short break schemes surveyed.
- General advice was given in more than half the schemes by manual handling trainers or advisors. However, advice on individual placements was given by the occupational therapist in the majority of schemes.
- The majority of schemes (78%) offered general moving and handling training to their carers. However, this type of training was difficult to access and take-up tended to be low.
- General moving and handling training for carers was mandatory in under half of the schemes surveyed (46%). In theory, over 80% of schemes offered specific training on individual placements. However, in reality, this training was difficult to access due to financial constraints and shortages of occupational therapists. Therefore, this training was frequently given by scheme staff and the child's parents.
- Seventy-eight per cent of schemes had access to advice from an occupational therapist. In the majority of instances this was free.
- Those schemes that were satisfied with the advice from an occupational therapist, as well as those that were not, expressed views about long waiting lists, lack of resources and staff shortages in occupational therapy services.
- Very few schemes (9%) had a written policy on the provision of aids and adaptations to carers. Schemes which had a separate budget for this provision found this budget only covered the purchase of small pieces of equipment.
- Thirty-five per cent of schemes have had to suspend a total of 89 placements during the past 12 months due to moving and handling difficulties.
- Fifty-two per cent of schemes had been prevented from making a total of 160 new placements because of moving and handling issues during the 12 months prior to the study.
- The number of schemes unable to make new placements was not a true reflection of the situation. Schemes reported that many

children were not ever referred to family-based schemes because the referrer was aware that a placement would not be found due to moving and handling difficulties. Children requiring moving and handling were often referred to residential short break services.

- A small number of schemes have found creative solutions to these difficulties. The main solution mentioned was the setting up of fee-paid or contract carers to offer short breaks to children who require moving and handling.
- The majority of schemes (85%) conduct risk assessments on children who require moving and handling. Risk assessments were carried out by scheme staff in the majority of instances. Occupational therapists carry out some of the risk assessments either on their own or jointly with the scheme worker.

The East Sussex judgment

A case in East Sussex ended in a landmark judgment in relation to moving and handling. The case focused on the needs of two young women with profound and multiple disabilities, named as 'A' and 'B'. They had had a five-year battle with East Sussex County Council after it introduced a blanket ban on care workers manually lifting any disabled or older person because of the risk of care workers suffering back or other injuries. Other equipment, such as hoists, was used to lift A and B, but it caused them pain and the two women asked to be lifted manually; this request was refused as it was deemed too 'hazardous' for the care workers. As a result, A and B's care package broke down and their parents were left to do all the lifting, with disregard to their own physical health.

The case challenged the reliance on the Royal College of Nursing guidance and suggested that the Health and Safety Executive guidance would be the most 'relevant' to home care situations and that it would be the most 'appropriate' guide, as it takes account of disabled people's human rights to dignity, freedom and independence.

The court emphasised the need for a balanced approach to the rights of the disabled person and the rights of workers to be protected by health and safety regulations. The imposing of a blanket ban on manual lifts represented a 'no risk regime', or a 'risk elimination regime', rather than one that seeks to offer independence and dignity to disabled people while minimising risk to workers. The court found that: 'There may be situations where some manual handling is an inherent feature in what the employee is employed to do.' The judge went on to say that 'in the present case, in my judgement, some manual handling is in any view an inherent – and inescapable – feature of the very task for which those who care for A and B are employed'.

In the case of routine lifts within the home, it is 'likely to be unlawful' for A and B's carers to:

- allow them to remain sitting in the bath for any really appreciable time without lifting them out
- leave them to sit on the lavatory for a long time
- leave them in a chair or elsewhere with the risk that bedsores will develop
- fail to pick them up if they fall and remain lying – particularly in a public place
- leave them sitting in bodily waste for any appreciable time.

The judge also stated that A and B had the right to participate in community life and that access to recreational activities is so important that a significant amount of manual handling might be required. Thus, it is 'likely to be unlawful' for a carer to:

- fail to take them out of the house (for example, to go swimming) merely because a power cut means the hoist is not working
- restrict the time available for such activities as shopping, swimming or horse riding because manual lifting would otherwise be required
- fail to take them swimming because the swimming baths do not have a hoist
- fail to take them shopping because

changing an incontinence pad may require a manual lift.

The judge made it clear that there may be some instances where lifting a disabled person may not be reasonably practicable, but that consideration should not be made without a thorough risk assessment which takes into account the impact on the disabled person, his or her wishes, feelings and human rights.

Bert Massie, Chairman of the Disability Rights Commission, said of the judgment: 'This is a clear victory for thousands of disabled people who have been denied their most basic of human rights. There is an obvious need for care workers not to be put at risk of injury in their jobs but this must be balanced with disabled people's independence and quality of life. Blanket bans on lifting all disabled people in the home have had a huge detrimental impact. We urge all local authorities to stop such practices and use health and safety guidance that puts disabled people's needs back at the heart of the care system.' (Disability Rights Commission, January 2003)

Policy guidance: what needs to be in place?

Service providers should attempt to cover all the following areas in their policies on moving and handling.

Risk assessment

As with other areas of risk, children who require moving and handling require a risk assessment of their needs. This should be carried out by the agency responsible for providing the service with advice, if available from others. Services should look for support from other settings where the child has their needs met, for example, at school. This initial assessment should be part of a process which looks at how the child's needs can be met and whether lifting and handling concerns may restrict service choice. This should be decided as part of a balanced approach between protecting the health and safety of staff and carers and upholding the rights and dignity of the child or young person.

Risk assessments for safer handling are clearly laid out in Manual Handling Operations Regulations 1992 (known as the 'TILE' assessment) and cover:

- the lifting task: why is it required, are there alternatives
- the young person's weight and needs: it is essential to build in a section on how much the child or young person can do for themselves and how they could help in any handling activities
- the physical environment: is it a safe place to lift, are there any hazards, do you have enough room, etc
- the individual capacities of the lifter: is the carer/worker fit enough to lift, are they experienced, etc. This reinforces the need for health information on staff/carers to ensure that they do not put themselves and the child at risk. Staff carrying out these assessments should be trained in their use.

Involve the child and family in the process

It is important when working with children and families to make the process as child centred as possible. Some moving and handling formats still refer to people as 'loads' with 'stresses' such as continence and spasms. The examples at the end of this section show that this can be changed to a format where the child is central and individual and their moving and handling needs are fully addressed. As well as helping to build a relationship with the child and family, carrying out the assessment can address issues such as the child's communication method and their level of comfort with procedures.

Assess the child's needs in a range of settings

As services have diversified, children may be assessed for a range of activities. This may include sitting or shared care, or leisure and play activities. This assessment process builds on the risk assessment and looks at areas where risk activity takes place. So the process agreed for one setting will be transferred to others.

Draw up a detailed moving and handling plan

All children with moving and handling needs should have a detailed plan before service delivery begins. The plan should cover all the activities the child might engage in while in the care of a particular service. This should include transfers, toileting arrangements, etc and may also include activities such as swimming or use of ball pools, etc. The plan should be clear and detailed enough to be understood by anyone who needs to use it. Plans need to be dated and regularly reviewed. They should be flexible enough for new activities to be added as necessary.

Training in moving and handling

All those involved with moving and handling should be trained. No member of staff, carer or volunteer should carry out any moving and handling procedure until they have received accredited training and have been deemed to be competent. Training should always be provided by an accredited trainer and cannot be cascaded. It is important that accredited trainers have experience in the specific moving and handling needs of children and this should be checked before they are engaged. Records of training received should be kept by service providers so that they are easily available for inspection purposes, and certificates of attendance should be issued. Opportunities to refresh and update the training must be regularly provided. The suggested minimum requirement for updates is two years.

Understanding safe and unsafe lifting

Training should cover both safe and unsafe lifting. The definition of unsafe lifts is not clear for children's services because lower weight guidance is not available. However,

there are some methods of lifting which have been shown to run high risks of injury to both the lifter and the person being lifted. It is unsafe to lift at arms length or at a distance from the body, either in front or to one side. This is because the body in this position causes the greatest risk of overstrain or overload. In light of this, the Royal College of Nursing suggested that these lifts should be banned. The four main unsafe lifts are:

- **The drag lift** This is any way of handling someone where the person's underarm is used as a handle to lift. While this lift is popular it has been proven to involve high levels of injuries to all concerned.
- **The orthodox lift** This lift, which has also been popular, was traditionally where two people stood either side of a bed and lifted someone by clasping their wrists under the person's back and thighs. Again, it results in unacceptably high levels of injuries.
- **Lifting when the person being lifted has their arms around the lifter's neck** Again, a slight fall would lead to a high level of injury.
- **The use of a pole and canvas stretcher** This is, hopefully, not applicable to community settings.

Equipment

It is important to remember that equipment, while useful, will not always provide a solution to every moving and handling situation.

When using equipment, services should ensure that it encourages and maximises the young person's independence rather than increasing dependency. Staff who use equipment should be trained in its usage. Services should look at the provision of small pieces of equipment. Many of these, sliding boards and transfer sheets for example, are relatively inexpensive and would therefore be reasonable for schemes to buy. Other pieces of generic equipment which can be used for children, such as lifting cushions, are more expensive but may be worth investment and discussion with equipment specialists. Child-specific equipment should not be purchased by schemes and the purchase of duplicate equipment – that is, equipment needed both at home and in placement – should be discussed with therapists working with the child. The implementation of ICES (Integrated Community Equipment Services) should improve the provision of community equipment to children and should, for example, supply portable hoists and communication equipment. Schemes should approach their regional implementation team member to check for developments in their area. For full details of ICES see their website: www.ices.org.uk.

When equipment is being used it is important that the service is clear about who is responsible for regular checking and maintenance.

Specific difficulties

It is inevitable within any service that there will be individual situations which are difficult and where standard solutions don't fit. Two examples are transport and activities.

Transport

There is no clear guidance on the transfer of children in and out of cars. Each situation will need to be resolved differently. For some children, the use of a swivel car seat or board might be an appropriate response, for others the use of wheelchair accessible vehicles, including black cabs, may be necessary. The service will need to ensure that transport issues are addressed as part of the moving and handling plan and that a separate record is kept of the transport needs of young people.

Activities

Services will want to promote the independence of children and young people by providing them with new experiences and activities. By their nature these activities are not likely to be covered by a generic moving and handling assessment and will need a separate risk assessment. The use of ball pools is an obvious example. There is no safe way of lifting a disabled child in and out of a ball pool but young people often find it a rewarding experience. Staff should note this in their assessments and try to find ways of providing the experience in a controlled way. When young people are involved in a range of outdoor activities, specialist advice should be sought.

Review, monitor and record

Services working with children and young people with moving and handling needs will need to have clear and accessible review and monitoring procedures.

Children's risk assessments and moving and handling plans should be reviewed every six months or sooner if major changes occur. Schemes should also keep a record of all training received by carers, staff and volunteers to ensure appropriate updates are offered. Schemes should also keep equipment logs and details of any maintenance and servicing required.

Services should also record when a child's needs cannot be met because of their moving and handling needs so that this can contribute to service planning.

Conclusion

Moving and handling presents a difficult challenge to services as is evidenced by the Shared Care Network study (Carlin 2003). The number of children with moving and handling needs continues to rise as children with the most complex needs survive and grow through childhood. In the midst of this, service providers have struggled with inadequate guidance and a culture of risk elimination. However, the recent East Sussex judgment and home care guidance issued by the HSE (2001) reinforce a position where the needs of disabled people and their carers can and must be balanced. The Disability Rights Commission is also interested in moving and handling issues and how they apply in community settings, and it is likely that further clarity will emerge over time.

The Integrated Community Equipment Services (ICES) programme offers a significant opportunity to improve community equipment provision and services should ensure that local implementation fully embraces the needs of children both at home and in community activities.

Many disabled children currently experience high levels of unmet need because of their moving and handling requirements, and service planners need to recognise and address this. New access requirements under the Disability Discrimination Act, which comes into force in 2004, may provide an impetus to focus on this group of children.

References

National Back Pain Association in collaboration with the Royal College of Nursing (1997) *The Guide to Handling Patients*, Fourth Edition

Sue Cunningham (2000) *Disability Oppression and Public Policy*

Jones and Lenehan (2000) *The effect of the Manual Handling Regulations on family based short break services*, Shared Care Network

Carlin J (2003) *Moving and Handling Survey*, Shared Care Network

Bert Massie, Chairman, Disability Rights Commission, press release, January 2003

Integrated Community Equipment Services website www.ices.org.uk

Health and Safety Executive (2001) *Handling Home Care: Achieving safe, efficient and positive outcomes for care workers and clients*

Checklist of key points: moving and handling

1   The agency responsible for providing the service must carry out a **risk assessment**.

2   Staff who carry out moving and handling risk assessments must receive **training**.

3   The child or young person must be **involved in the process**.

4   The risk assessment must include the child or young person's needs **in each setting** that service is provided.

5   Draw up a detailed **moving and handling plan**.

6   Provide **accredited training** for all carers and staff who will be involved in moving and handling.

7   Ensure that all care providers are aware of **safe and unsafe lifts**.

8   Remember that **equipment**, while useful, will not always provide the solution.

9   There is no clear guidance on **transport and transfer** of children in and out of cars. Each situation needs individual risk assessment and solution.

10 **Review, monitor and record** moving and handling activity through clear and accessible reviewing and monitoring procedures.

Appendix   The law in detail

Health and Safety at Work Act 1974

Employers must:
- protect the health and safety of their employees
- protect the health and safety of others who might be affected by the way they go about their work
- prepare a statement of safety policy and the organisation and arrangements for carrying it out.

Management of Health and Safety at Work Regulations 1992

Employers must:
- assess health and safety risks to employees and others, to identify the precautions required by health and safety law
- take particular account in their assessment of risks to new and expectant mothers and to their unborn and breastfeeding babies
- make arrangements for planning, organising, controlling, monitoring and reviewing the precautions required by law
- provide appropriate health surveillance
- appoint competent people to help them comply with health and safety law
- provide employees with adequate training and instructions
- co-operate and co-ordinate with other employers where they share premises or workplaces.

Manual Handling Operations Regulations 1992

Definition:
Manual handling is defined by the Health and Safety Executive as 'any transporting or supporting of a load, including lifting, lowering, pushing, pulling, carrying or moving by hand or bodily force'.
  Employers have a duty to:
- avoid the need for staff to carry out manual handling where there is a risk or injury

- assess manual handling operations that cannot be avoided
- reduce the risks as far as is reasonably practicable.
  Employees should:
- exercise care and use common sense
- follow employers' instructions, policies and procedures
- inform the employer of any medical condition, including pregnancy, which may affect the ability to carry out safe handling practice
- report accidents and incidents, or near misses

PUWER (Provision and Use of Work Equipment Regulations 1998)

These regulations apply to any equipment which is used by an employee at work, including equipment such as hoists. They set out the employer's duty to ensure that equipment is:
- suitable for intended use
- safe for use
- used only by people who have received adequate information, instruction and training.

LOLER (Lifting Operations and Lifting Equipment Regulations 1998)

These regulations contain specific requirements relating to equipment which is used by an employee at work, which includes lifting equipment such as hoists and bath lifts.
  Employers have a duty to:
- provide training for staff on the use of all lifting equipment by a competent person
- provide instructions with the equipment
- ensure that equipment and accessories for lifting people are checked by a competent person every six months
- carry out a risk assessment on the use of all equipment and make staff aware of the risks.

Sample forms and guidance

Forms and guidance in relation to moving and handling are beginning to be developed in child- and person-centred formats. This handbook brings together a selection of good practice forms from around the UK.

   The following is a list of forms included in this chapter, and what they are used for. The forms were supplied by different organisations and local authorities, and have been adapted for publication in this handbook. They are intended to be examples of good practice and can be copied or adapted for use by other organisations. Copies of originals can be obtained from Shared Care Network.

Form 1 Moving and handling assessment. This form shows that moving and handling assessments can be child-centred while fulfilling health and safety criteria. NCH Caring Together Lincolnshire

Form 2 Moving and handling risk assessment and individual handling care plan. This form illustrates an assessment which covers each of the settings in which a child may need moving and handling support. Barnardo's Grove Park Service Harrogate

Form 3 Moving and handling training schedule. An example of a training programme. Chailey Heritage School

Form 4 Record of moving and handling training. This shows how the training in Form 3 is recorded.

Form 5 Protocol for working arrangements between the occupational therapy service and Barnardo's Somerset Inclusion Service. A useful protocol looking at specific agency responsibilities

Form 6 Completed moving and handling assessment. An example of a detailed assessment which provides practical information while remaining person-centred. Cambridge

Form 7 Principles of moving and handling. A very useful guide developed by Carole Jackson, an independent occupational therapist in Cambridgeshire, and reproduced with kind permission.

Form 8 Risk assessment for children who may require moving and handling. The first of two forms developed by South Gloucestershire Council Social Services Department looking at child-centred assessment.

Form 9 This form takes the assessment forward to look at handling techniques.

Form 1

NCH Caring Together, Lincolnshire

Child's details

Name _____ Date of birth _____

Weight _____ Height _____

Medical diagnosis/details _____

NCH carer details

Name _____

Address _____

_____

_____ Telephone _____

Details of physical limitations _____

NCH link worker _____

Details of handling constraints

_____

_____

Equipment used

_____

_____

Movement hazards

Physical

_____

_____

Communication/comprehension/behaviour

_____

_____

Additional information/comments

_____

_____

The dignity of risk

Moving and handling care plan

Task	Movement method	Equipment/aids	Number of people

Assessment completed by

Name _____   Signature _____

Date _____   Review date _____

Problems/deficiencies

Details of remaining problems/deficiencies	Action/measures needed	Agency/person informed

Assessor's signature and date _____

Date resolved _____

Form 2

Barnardo's Grove Road Service, Harrogate

For _____ Date of birth _____

Address _____

_____ Postcode _____

Phone _____

Parent/guardian permission to share information between relevant agencies

Signed _____ Date _____

Relationship to child _____

Agencies which may share this information _____

Moving and handling risk assessment

Where?	Completed	Assessed by	Requested	Date
Home				
Inclusive playscheme				
School				
Short breaks carers				
Resource centre				
Other (state where)				

Is it envisaged that a moving and handling risk assessment will be required in the near future?

For what activity	Carer involved	Place	Date of review

Assessment review

Activity	Date	Place	Assessor

Handling constraints

Describe relevant physical needs, including sensory impairment needs	Equipment/appliances used

Describe relevant medical information	Surgical appliances

Describe communication and comprehension	Methods of communication used

83

Describe emotional and behavioural difficulties	Techniques to be used

Child's views/wishes, eg preferred methods of handling, toileting, feeding

How, when and by whom were these obtained? _____

Signed _____ Date _____

Personal information

Weight _____ Date _____

Height _____ Date _____

Cultural/religious considerations

Form 3

Chailey Heritage School

Training for all staff is presented in two sessions, and each is adapted to suit the audience. For example, because administrative, domestic and maintenance staff are not involved in the handling of pupils, their training does not include the session on handling of people and the use of equipment with which other employees must be familiar.

The theoretical session covers:
- introduction of the topic of manual handling
- legislation
- spinal awareness
- risk assessment
- inanimate objects
- handling people.

The practical session covers:
- observation of and familiarisation with aids and equipment, their purpose and how to use them
- observation of and familiarisation with movement of loads, including pushing wheelchairs
- practical training in the use of aids and equipment
- practical training in the movement of loads.

Questions are addressed during the summary sessions of 20–35 minutes which follow each practical training session.

Timetables for each staff group training session are available from manual handling trainers.

Form 4

Chailey Heritage School

Name _____

Job title _____

Place of work _____ Employee number _____

Part 1   Theory

Legislation	
Spinal awareness	
Risk assessment	
Inanimate objects	
Handling people	
Date of theory training	

Trainer's signature _____

Part 2   Practical

	Observed	Practised	
Hoist familiarisation	Yes/no	Yes/no	
Lifting and handling	Yes/no	Yes/no	
How to avoid back pain	Yes/no	Yes/no	
Right and wrong ways of lifting	Yes/no	Yes/no	

Employee signature _____ Date _____

Manual handling trainer _____ Date _____

You may wish to retain a copy of this document for your personal reference.

The original will be retained on your personal file.

Moving and handling

Form 5

Barnardo's Somerset Inclusion Service

Scope

This protocol covers all activities in Somerset in relation to:
- general hazard risk assessment of carers' homes
- moving and handling risk assessment
- moving and handling training
- provision, management and servicing of equipment supplied to carers' for use with children referred to Family Link.

Purpose

- To meet the required standards to provide a safe and positive environment for disabled children
- To provide clarity about the respective roles and responsibilities of SSD staff and Barnardo's staff in this area of work

Responsibilities – general

Somerset Social Services Department and Somerset Area Health Authority have delegated responsibility for management of family-based care for children with complex health care needs and disability to Barnardo's Somerset Inclusion Project (SIP) Family Link. SIP Family Link will take responsibility for the implementation of any recommendations made following manual handling assessments.

This protocol forms part of the Service Level Agreement and is monitored by the partner agencies as part of the regular Service Level Agreement reviews

Specific responsibilities of each agency

Barnardo's	Somerset Social Services
A General hazard risk assessment • Family Link resource workers will undertake to complete General Hazard Risk Assessments using the current Barnardo's format: Hazard Risk Checklist – Family Placements. They will alert appropriate parties to the actions required and follow up to ensure compliance. • All carers will be supplied with smoke and carbon monoxide alarms. • Resource workers will be updated at the time of the carers' reviews. **Note** Carers' assessment for approval and Hazard Risk Checklist will indicate if carers are living and working under reasonable safety standards such that one would expect in a family home – it is not intended to replicate residential provision.	

The dignity of risk

Barnardo's	Somerset Social Services

B Moving and handling training
- Will organise moving and handling training and regular updates for carers and staff.

- Will provide a manual handling trainer.

C Moving and handling risk assessment and follow up
- Make a written referral to occupational therapist (OT).

- OTs to follow up referral and complete an assessment with recommendations within a mutually agreed timescale. This could involve: carer familiarisation with equipment; recommendation for management of specific needs of child, etc.
- To liaise with firms supplying equipment recommended and meet with them in the carers' homes.

- Alert OTs to any relevant changes in circumstances, eg change of carer.

- Review with carers the equipment and management needs following changes in the environment or in the child's physical needs; or annually if no other changes identified.
- Following review, inform by report or attend child's review as necessary.

D Building adaptations
- Make all arrangements re: building adaptations to comply with OT recommendations and inform OTs when work completed.

- OTs to make written recommendations in respect of adaptations required to carers' homes and check when work is completed.

E Vehicles
- Barnardo's to ensure that all Barnardo's-owned vehicles are regularly checked and serviced according to Barnardo's standards of good practice and legal requirements.
- In respect of carers' vehicles which have been adapted using Barnardo's Family Link funds:
  - The carers take responsibility for checks and servicing.
  - Barnardo's will underwrite additional cost resulting from adaptations, eg lift maintenance.
- Alert OTs to changes and issues requiring management.

- OTs to advise with recommendations following assessment re: appropriate equipment and management.

Moving and handling

Form 6

Cambridge

Moving and handling assessment – people

Name <u>*John*</u>   Date _____

Build *Large*   Height *Estimate 120 cm*   Weight *Estimate 38 kg*

Mobility *Able to walk unaided when well, able to walk and stand if unwell, but needing lots of support.*

Summary

In general John visits twice a month and stays overnight. When John is feeling well, he needs minimal guidance and assistance. However, he can be very variable in his abilities and it is this variability that places any person looking after him at high risk of injury. It is difficult to predict when and to what degree John may have a seizure.

From a moving and handling perspective, the best solution would be to make sure that drug treatment is effective at reducing the number and severity of the seizures and I understand that this is being attempted at the moment.

In the immediate term, John should not use the stairs if he appears to be unwell and especially as John grows, the need for him to climb stairs should be eliminated.

When John is feeling less able to assist, then transfers should be kept to a minimum, until John is able to perform them independently. In particular this applies to getting into and out of the bath and getting into and out of a car.

Barbara, his carer, has attended manual handling training courses in the past and understood the risk assessment process. John is already quite heavy for his age, which increases the risk of injury to Barbara should he start to have a seizure, especially on the stairs. Barbara was more than happy to reduce the transfers, when/if John was unwell.

The 'outcomes' section of this form should be completed as a review of this assessment and should be completed if any circumstances change.

Handling constraints, eg disability, weakness, pain, etc

John has epileptic seizures. They tend to occur in clusters and he may be unconscious from a few seconds to 3–4 minutes. Rectal Valium is to be administered after 5 minutes, although Barbara has never had to give this. John may suddenly drop or may have a tonic/clonic-type seizure (muscles will become very tight and in both cases John will be unconscious). There is no recognisable pattern and he may not have any seizures for a while and then have 3–4 in one day. How John feels afterwards is also variable. He may sleep, be unsteady on his feet or be ready to carry on.

John also wears ankle splints to help support his feet and should wear these when walking.

John has put on a large amount of weight recently.

Problems with communication, predictability, etc.

John has not been heard talking, but in general is quiet if he is unhappy and noisy if he is content. If he wants something or does not want something he can indicate by pointing.

Environmental hazards

John sleeps upstairs. There is a turn at the top of the stairs which he can manage when he feels well.

John sleeps in a bed against the wall, which he can get into unaided when he is well.

The bathroom and bedroom have sliding doors which gives more space to move. The bath has a wall on three sides. John can get into the bath with minimal assistance when well.

Moving and handling assessment

Task	Risks identified	Action plan
Stairs	John is steady on the stairs when he is well and at the time of the assessment John had no difficulties managing the stairs. He did sit down at one point but was safe and managed to stand himself up again. However, Barbara and John would be at high risk of injury if John was using the stairs during and after suffering the effects of a seizure.	In the very short term, John should not use the stairs unless he is obviously independent and steady. This, however, would still leave Barbara and John at a high risk of an injury if John had a seizure while on the stairs. As John grows and gets heavier the risk will increase. The plan therefore should be to eliminate the need to climb stairs. An interim plan, discussed with Barbara, would be that if John became unsteady, then if he was upstairs he would remain there until well enough to move independently and if he was downstairs to remain there until able to move independently.
Bathing	When John is able to help there is a low risk of injury. However, if he is unwell this changes to high risk.	John should not be assisted into the bath if he is unwell. Please ensure that there is a secure bath mat in the bath. If John becomes unwell while in the bath, remove the water and keep him as warm and dry as possible. Wait to see if John recovers sufficiently to move himself out of the bath. If you are concerned call for assistance.
Assisting into and out of bed	John is independent in this task if he is well. If he needs help Barbara is at high risk of an injury.	Avoid transfers as far as possible when John is feeling unsteady. Keep close to him at all times while assisting him. You may find it helpful to stand to the side and slightly behind when helping him.
Personal care	John is usually changed on the bed and can assist to roll. There is a risk of injury due to potential stooping and twisting.	Keep close and practice working 'on the angle', which decreases the risk of twisting. This means standing at an angle to the bed with the feet slightly apart in an offset position. Some people find a knee on the bed helpful. The risk would be significantly reduced if John could be changed on a height-adjustable change table.

Moving and handling

Task	Risks identified	Action plan
Sit to stand sequence	John is independent when well, but unsteady when he has had a seizure. The risk of injury to Barbara and John will be increased if attempting to perform a transfer.	Avoid transfers as far as possible when John is unsteady. If John becomes unsteady while transferring, keep close, stand slightly behind and to the side. Place the closer arm low down his back – this gives support. Your other arm can be placed on the outside of his shoulder or under the forearm – keeping this close to his body.
On/off floor	John should not be manually lifted from the floor at any time, except in an emergency as described in The Guide to Handling Patients (National Back Pain Association – see references, page 76). There is a high risk of injury to Barbara and John.	John should only be moved from the floor using mechanical equipment such as a hoist, if he is able to support himself or use a blow-up cushion or seat. If John is unwell he should stay on the floor until he is able to move himself safely.
Transport	John is able to climb into a car independently. Barbara and John are at high risk if he is manually lifted into and out of a car.	Please avoid car journeys if John is feeling unwell or is still recovering from a seizure. If John has a seizure in the car, do not move him until he is able. Follow the protocol for administering rectal Valium if this is required.
Handling during and after a seizure	John and Barbara are at high risk of injury if in particular John has a seizure while in the process of standing or using stairs.	As far as possible avoid handling or moving John if he is having a seizure. Protect his head. Keep as close as possible.

Moving and handling assessment – outcomes

Task	Outcome	Revised action plan
Stairs		
Bathing		
Assisting into and out of bed		
Personal care		
Sit to stand sequence		
On/off floor		
Transport		
Handling during and after a seizure		

Assessed by _____

Accepted by _____

Date _____

The dignity of risk

Form 7

(A very useful guide developed by Carole Jackson, an independent occupational therapist in Cambridgeshire, and reproduced with kind permission)

It is important to be able to measure the moving and handling against a standard. The following principles will help you check whether the task you are doing is safe or will help highlight the dangers. Your aim is to adhere to the nine principles as far as possible.

1 Assess

- Have you checked the written risk assessment?
- Have you made an 'on the spot' assessment NOW?
- Are there any additional factors that will make the task more dangerous?

2 Plan

- If you discover that there are added risks or you decide it is NOT safe to continue you must stop – get help and re-assess.

3 Communication

- Have you talked to the person you are helping? Keep talking to them
- Have you talked to other relevant people? Do you know the full story?

4 Attitude

- How are you approaching this task – are you tired, cross?
- Is your attitude going to have a negative effect on the task?

5 Keep close

- You can lift more if the load is close to your centre of gravity.
- Check – where is your centre of gravity in this task?
- You must still work within your own individual capability.

6 Foot position

- You should always aim to work within your base area.
- Your feet need to be positioned so that you can move them to maintain balance.
- You should start with the base small and offset, the weight even through both feet.

7 Hand hold

- Avoid using your fingertips when holding a person – use the palm of your hand.
- Check – is there also tension in your shoulders?
- Is your hold indirect?

8 Head first

- Before you start the task, make sure that your head goes first (ie the movement that you, and the person you are helping, are doing should start from the head).
- Make sure you use a clear and specific command to start.

9 Flow

- The transfer or movement should be smooth. You should not feel discomfort or feel you cannot manage. Do not use speed and strength to complete a task.
- If it does not flow, re-assess.

Moving and handling

Form 8

South Gloucestershire Council Social Services Department

This form must be completed for all children who may require moving and handling where this involves a significant risk of injury. The assessment should be reviewed when circumstances change, or at the review of service provision/care plan, or at least annually.

The assessment must be communicated and accessible to all parents/carers and staff who may be involved with the child's care, and the original must be kept on the child's file. All foster/family link carers and department staff must be familiar with the social services policy for the moving and handling of children, which is available in the Council's Health and Safety Manual.

Child's name _____ Date of birth _____

Home address _____

_____

_____

Address of assessed environment _____

_____

_____

Date of assessment _____ Form completed by _____

Child's medical condition _____

Height _____ Weight _____

Does the child understand the need for moving and handling? _____

Does the child assist the helper with moving and handling? _____

Can the child bear weight:

a) with support? _____ b) unaided? _____

Can the child walk if supported? _____

Does the child require support to maintain balance when sitting? _____

Other factors affecting moving and handling (please give details) _____

Pain/risk of dislocation if moved _____ Fatigue _____

Fragility _____ Spasm _____

Sensory loss _____ Skin condition _____

Epilepsy _____ Fear – specify _____

Floppy _____ History of falls _____

Other – specify _____

Does the child use any of the following? (please tick if applicable):

Buggy	☐	Splints/other	☐	Manual wheelchair	☐	Spinal jacket	☐
Standing frame	☐	Powered wheelchair	☐	Hoist to bath	☐	Hoist to bed	☐
Supportive seating	☐	Walking aid	☐	Plaster	☐	Stair lift	☐
Toilet aid	☐						

Other – specify _____

Working environment – specify different rooms if applicable

1 Space constraints preventing good posture _____

2 Uneven/slippery floors _____

3 Variations in floor/work surface levels _____

4 Problems with heating/ventilation _____

5 Poor lighting conditions _____

6 Space constraints in transport _____

Task/type of transfer where assistance is required

Task/type of transfer	Equipment used	What does task involve (see list below – specify 1–9)	Level of risk (high, medium, low)
Chair to chair			
Chair to standing position			
Floor to chair			
Floor to standing position			
In and out of bath			
In and out of bed/turning in bed			
Support in walking			
Up/down stairs			
In and out of car			
On/off toilet			
Changing incontinence pad			
Other			

Does the task involve:

1 Holding child away from trunk ☐

2 Twisting ☐

3 Stooping ☐

4 Excessive lifting or lowering distances ☐

5 Excessive carrying or moving distances ☐

6 Strenuous pushing or pulling ☐

7 Risk of sudden movement from the child, eg spasm ☐

8 Frequent or prolonged physical effort ☐

9 Risk of resistance from child, eg verbal/physical ☐

Moving and handling

Individual capability – does the task:

1 Overstretch the staff/carer's physical capabilities? ☐

2 Present a hazard to those with health problems? ☐

3 Present a hazard to those who are pregnant? ☐

4 Require special information and training? ☐

Other factors

Is movement or posture restricted by personal protective clothing? _____

Other comments _____

_____

_____

Overall risk assessment   high/medium/low

For identified hazards, list preventive action in order of priority based on level of risk:

Preventive action	By whom	When
1		
2		
3		
4		

If further assessment of moving/handling equipment will be required, specify probable age/development stage when review/new assessment will be needed:

Signed by _____

Job title _____

The dignity of risk

Form 9

South Gloucestershire Council Social Services Department

Moving and handling techniques

Transfer for	Equipment for transfer	No. of carers	Techniques recommended	Precautions necessary/ risks highlighted
Lifting on/ off floor		1	Get down to Sam's level by first kneeling close to him. Roll or slide Sam onto your lap. Position him close to your body using a firm comfortable handhold and supporting his head. Raise up onto one knee (see attached diagram) and adjust your body weight to maintain your balance if necessary. Reverse technique to put Sam on floor.	Try to keep this transfer to a minimum. Hold Sam centrally, do not twist your spine. Use your legs and knees when reaching and lifting: avoid bending your back.
Carrying on level and up/down stairs		1	Keep the length of time Sam is carried as short as possible. Plan the journey beforehand, make sure there are no obstacles in the way and any doors/ stairgates are open. Hold Sam close to your body, facing and chest to chest If needed, rest arm against banister or wall when coming downstairs for support.	As above, also: Only carry Sam when necessary, use wheeled equipment if available. Get someone to help carry Sam up and down stairs.
Nappy changing, dressing/ undressing	Bed guards	1	Nappy changing/dressing/ undressing downstairs to be done on floor. Nappy changing/dressing/ undressing/upstairs to be done on bed. Lower bed guards in advance of transferring Sam on/off bed. Place him towards edge of bed to avoid over-reaching during task. Raise bed guard if moving away from bed, even momentarily while Sam is on it. Sam's body brace to be sent to school/home in bag (ie not fitted by carer in morning).	Ensure all changing equipment, towels, etc are close by beforehand. Carer should try to maintain a straight back during the task and avoid twisting movements. If Sam is having a tantrum keep him safe and just do essential tasks.

Moving and handling

Transfer for	Equipment for transfer	No. of carers	Techniques recommended	Precautions necessary/ risks highlighted
Bath			Sam to be strip washed only.	See precautions above. Remain aware of back care at all times.
Sitting with Sam on lap		1	Sit in well supported position on chair or on floor. If sitting on settee ensure Sam's head is next to settee arm. Use pillows/cushions for extra support if needed. If sitting on floor carer's back should be fully supported, eg against settee. Use pillows/cushions for extra support if needed. Sam can be place in a long legged sitting position, between carer's legs with his back and head supported against carer's chest. Keep this activity to minimum, eg for giving comfort or a bottle.	Carer to maintain good posture and straight back during activity. Avoid twisting movements. Have any equipment needed close to hand.
Feeding	High chair/ wheelchair (being provided from wheelchair clinic)	1	Carer to make sure that they have a stable base and good posture when lifting Sam in and out of the high chair or wheelchair. Wheelchair brakes to be on during transfers. Make sure Sam is sitting with his bottom well back in seat and that his hips and knees are level. Fasten lap straps firmly. Fasten any other straps, eg across chest or on feet. Carer to sit on chair at suitable height for feeding.	Back care precautions as above. Sam should normally have his body support and shoes on when sitting in the chair to maintain an upright, symmetrical posture.
Car	Britax car seat	1	Use Britax car seat on front seat *if no air bag fitted to car.* Front seat to be slid backwards as far as possible to allow easier access to car seat during transfers. Carer to make sure they have a stable base and good posture when lifting Sam in and out of car seat. Fasten straps securely.	Back care precautions as above.

The dignity of risk

5 Physical interventions for challenging behaviour/ managing behaviour

This chapter covers
Policy guidance
Policy for Shared Care services
Managing risk and physical interventions
Policy guidance: what needs to be in place?
Conclusion
References
Checklist of key points: restrictive physical interventions
Appendix: Policy guidance in detail
Sample forms and guidance

Managing behaviour is a specific task when caring for some children. The written policies and procedures for managing behaviour must be compatible and support the wider task of caring. They must direct the practice of assessment, planning, recording and monitoring and make the links between general and reactive planning.

General behaviour change planning is aimed at sustaining positive behaviour or preventing deterioration. These aims can be directed towards planning the programmes and the environment around the strengths of the child, alleviating behaviour problems and preventing crises before they occur. Planning needs to include identified risks and antecedent events so that triggers can be avoided as well as identified methods to get positive gain out of the consequences of negative behaviour that may occur. For example, if you were working with a child with autistic spectrum disorder, you would need to know the triggers – for example, dogs – and the distracter, videos, which would calm the child down.

Planning needs to encompass how to deal with emergency situations as part of an overall behaviour plan which states the ways

the young person and their family wish significant risk to be managed. The plan should concentrate on how we intervene early to prevent negative behaviour escalating and on how to use minimum physical interventions in order to contain such behaviour.

Contained risks are a necessary part of life. Some experimentation is necessary for children to experience their own self-control and the boost to self-esteem that this brings. This requires accurate and appropriate prescribing of the management of behaviour and the thresholds for interventions as identified by individualised risk assessments. Such judgement needs to be guided by very clear policy and practice guidelines and supplemented with training adapted to the setting, provided by an accredited trainer, which not only plans for success but encourages the experience of empathy for the child.

Policy guidance

There are two important references for the management of behaviour and physical intervention: *Joint Guidance on the Use of Restrictive Physical Interventions for Staff Working with Children and Adults who display Extreme Behaviour in Association with Learning and/or Autistic Spectrum Disorders* (DfES and DH 2002) and the *Code of practice for trainers in the use of physical interventions* (BILD 2001). This chapter includes guidance from both sources among its good practice guidelines. Detailed policy guidance is contained in the appendix at the end of this chapter.

The DfES/DH guidance is the culmination of all preceding legislation and comes with a common set of principles for use across all children's settings aimed to ensure children experience a co-ordinated and consistent approach from key services as they move from one setting to another. It is specific about all aspects surrounding behaviour management and physical intervention. Although written for a particular group of children, it is relevant for all settings – especially for children with severe emotional and behavioural difficulties. The guidance is not intended to cover all forms of extreme behaviour in all settings and there remain some differences allowed for in educational settings.

If service providers are guided by both the DfES/DH guidance and the work of BILD, whose conclusions have been based upon a wide evidence base and are applicable to a range of settings, they will be taking the right steps to ensure that their policy and practice minimises risk, is effective and safe, and provides a consistent approach to ensuring the dignity of children and staff alike.

BILD acknowledges that all interventions carry some risk – physical, emotional or legal – and emphasises that 'used in isolation physical interventions can easily become self-maintaining; they are an effective response once the behaviour has occurred, but because they do nothing to promote other forms of behaviour, they increase the chances that the challenging behaviour itself will be repeated'.

Policies for Shared Care services

Written policies should be clear and simple. Additional information covering specific areas requiring explanation or greater guidance should be kept in an appendix. The DfES/DH (2002) guidance states that there must be an individual plan for each child which identifies risks and the specific strategies or techniques that will be used.

Policies written by Shared Care services for behaviour management and the related physical interventions policy should set out the broad range of strategies which are approved for use. These should include

scenarios of common incidents. Children and families need to be included in the planning, monitoring and reviewing of individual and service policies and plans so that their concerns and preferences may be acted upon.

According to the BILD policy framework (John Harris *et al* 1996) behaviour management and physical intervention require effective leadership, caring relationships, shared goals, and excellent communication. Management must ensure systems are structured, appropriately detailed and used. Using the BILD policy framework will ensure that sound principles underpin policy, practice and individual decisions regarding intervention. The BILD publication sets out nine policy categories:

- **legal responsibilities of the service and the legal protections of users**
- **the values and ethical standards that guide any decision to use, or not, physical interventions** – covering best interests of the young person; fairness, courtesy and respect; being involved and supported in choices, decisions and learning which affect their lives
- **how preventive strategies and alternative approaches minimise physical interventions** – careful management and modification of the environment; meeting personal needs and conditions allows for non-physical interventions before children become violent; individualised strategies for responding to incidents of violence and reckless behaviour, including directions for the physical interventions to be used ensuring the safety of all concerned
- **the steps taken to ensure physical interventions are always used in the best interests of the service user** – using physical interventions only in conjunction with other strategies designed to help learn alternative non-challenging behaviours and when justified in respect of: what is known of the child from a formal multidisciplinary assessment; alternative approaches which have been tried; an evaluation of the potential risks involved;

The dignity of risk

reference to a body of expert knowledge and established good practice; strategy is regularly reviewed

- **the risks for young people, staff and members of the public and how can these be minimised** – potential hazards associated with the use of physical interventions should be systematically explored using a risk assessment procedure. Physical interventions should not involve unreasonable risk

- **how physical interventions are used without compromising the safety or well-being of service users** – minimum reasonable force and duration of time consistent with the young person's best interests; no pain; approved for use after individual assessments to identify contra-indications; and following any physical intervention there should be an assessment of injury or psychological distress

- **what service managers do to ensure that policies are properly implemented** – responsible for developing and implementing policies on the use of physical interventions and setting out written guidance for staff; ensure all incidents are clearly, comprehensively and promptly recorded; consider how to use the resources available for safe and effective physical interventions; ensure all children and their families or representatives have ready access to an effective complaints procedure

- **the responsibilities employers and managers have towards staff** – the safety and well-being of staff; encouraging staff to monitor all physical interventions and report any incidents which give cause for concern

- **how staff training assists in the development of good practice** – regular training on knowledge, skills and values from an instructor with appropriate experience and qualifications helps to ensure that staff only use interventions for which they have been trained and that all staff can respond to any incident which requires physical intervention.

Managing risk and physical interventions

24-hour management plans

The most effective intervention for behaviour is the creation of a safe and nurturing environment for each child in which they can feel contained yet free to explore. The sustaining of this continuity of care requires detailed individual assessment, planning and delivery in the form of a 24-hour management plan.

These individual plans are written to ensure that each day is centred around the needs and strengths of the young person. There are specific plans for important aspects, times and routines: getting up/breakfast, transitions, education, lunchtime, evening/bedtime, likes/dislikes, significant routines, leisure, special food/events, triggers to be avoided. Others can be added to match the child's needs.

For family- and community-based services this means, for example, that the service should look at adopting whatever behavioural management approach the school is using. This will recreate a feeling of security for the child and ensure our ways of managing behaviour are compatible. Different systems might confuse a child and actually make behaviour worse.

Environment

The environment needs to be adapted to meet the needs of the child so that they do not become stressed by having to adapt to each different setting. Focus should be on needs not wants and firm decisions made about what is to be included or excluded. Only when the current environment is successfully managed by the young person should there be discussion about introducing new things with the child and family.

Each of the five senses needs to be considered, balancing personal preference with positive outcome. These need to be taken into consideration in relation to the environment in general and to tasks and activities. Firm decisions are necessary regarding general factors such as intensity and duration as well as individual aspects of each:

- touch – what and how to make things available, advisability
- taste – taste can be a support for positive and negative behaviours
- smell – managed personal preference aromas that focus attention
- sight – brightness, colour and business
- hearing – communication, quiet environment or background sounds.

In community and family-based services, this means asking some key questions about matching and service provision:

- Do we have appropriate detailed information on the child and their environment?
- Is the child used to an outside play space?
- Does the child respond well or badly to dogs, other children, etc?
- Does the child have hypersensitive hearing (a common condition in Autistic Spectrum Disorder)?

Assessment

It is very important to systematically record every incident of problematic behaviour, whether physical intervention was used or not. This creates a greater understanding of the child and leads to better assessment and management of such incidents in the future.

Information needs to be simple and related to the child as an individual. In order that anyone meeting a child for the first time will be able to provide consistency, the following information about the child in a settled environment should be written down:

- the child's needs, and how meeting these needs helps the child settle through providing an environment and relationships that will create equilibrium
- what is stressful for the child and how to avoid these experiences or, where unavoidable, how to plan for them
- any transition needs preparation in advance, support while making and praise afterwards
- behaviours of the child that indicate that stress is being experienced and how to

respond to reduce it

- the diversionary or de-escalation strategies that will work for this child
- the early intervention strategies to be used
- the physical intervention strategies to be used
- the method of debriefing which allows this child to express her/his views about incidents and to learn from them.

For family and community services this means a detailed assessment process working with both family and school. It will also mean a longer introduction period into the service to ensure confidence on all sides.

Thresholds

The DfES/DH joint guidance and BILD advice state which interventions can be used and not used. Thresholds for intervention need to be similarly unambiguous and specific to the setting and known to everyone.

Thresholds will be different for each child. These need to be explored by the child, family and significant others involved in their care then put into a written plan that cannot be misunderstood and which is known to everyone concerned. This can be monitored and reviewed regularly by these same people. If a certain behaviour occurs there needs to be clear plans about what can and cannot be done. This gives the child the comfort of knowing what will happen. It also provides physical protection and the emotional comfort of planned, expected responses, initially to divert and de-escalate, and physically only if necessary.

At these early stages when children might test out the plans, it is important for adults to model what the children are being guided to achieve: understanding, correcting, resolving. Acknowledge that the child is struggling, praise them for persistence and then offer support. Children will learn that limits are set, rewards and sanctions are received, and the world is a safe place where they can be understood and contained.

Each behaviour management plan for each child will be different. The common training pattern for risk management is as important here as it is in invasive health care. Carers

The dignity of risk

should have general behaviour management/Autistic Spectrum Disorder training with an accredited trainer. They should then work with the family and school to ensure child-specific information is clear.

Physical interventions

In managing a child's behaviour there needs to be a scale of interventions. These should begin with the simplest: praising a child for good behaviour and providing distractions to ensure that boredom does not lead to poor behaviour. Full information about the child, along with a plan for managing behaviour, should keep the risk low and ensure that any intervention is proportionate and reasonable.

For each child there must be a written plan for physical interventions that describes the following:
- behaviour sequences and settings that may require a physical response
- the results of an assessment to determine any contraindications for its use
- a risk assessment that balances use of physical intervention against not using it
- a record of the views of families
- previous methods used without success
- the sanctioned techniques to be used
- staff/carers who are seen as competent to use them
- the method of reviewing the policy.

There are some interventions that are high risk: using mechanical means, holding on the floor, impeding airways, seclusion, and pressure on joints, airways, neck, chest, abdomen or groin. Emergency breakaway or disengagement techniques are high risk and must always use the least intrusive method and minimal pain. These methods need to be described in the policies and plans, which should also list unacceptable practices.

Restriction of liberty is permissible only in very specific circumstances, proportional to risk, and if for longer than a few minutes or more frequently than once a week then mental health or child care statutory powers are needed.

Only where medication is indicated in the care plan can it be routinely used, and care plans need to indicate any contraindications.

Routine rapid tranquillising should not be used as a method of gaining control over children who display violence or aggression. Further information is to be found in the DfEE Circular 14/96 'Supporting pupils with medical needs in school.'

Supporting pupils with medical needs
Therapeutic devices, wheelchairs for example, should not be used to prevent challenging negative behaviour, although they may be used to manage risks. In that case, their use needs to be agreed in advance with families and advocates and be recorded in the care plan.

Training
Physical interventions generally occur at the moment when both the child and adult are stressed and worried about losing control. Appropriate training is crucially important for knowing how to handle such occasions. Training in managing violence and aggression will explain the de-escalation, prevention, and communication skills necessary for preventing violent incidents and will be followed by the course in methods of physical intervention to be used when other strategies have failed.

To remain calm at times of crisis carers and staff need to be well practised in the application of approved techniques. Techniques need to be learned and need follow-up refreshers. Risks to a young person increase substantially if a technique is not performed correctly.

It is important to note that the cascade model for this training is not effective and training must be provided by accredited trainers.

BILD provides a checklist of key topics that should be covered in any training course:
- positive values in work with people with challenging behaviour
- legal responsibilities of staff and protection for service users
- physical interventions policy of the commissioning organisation
- primary prevention; secondary prevention
- developing positive behaviours

- using only those intervention techniques approved by the commissioning organisation
- principles of least restrictive intervention and gradient of control
- teamwork
- recording and monitoring.

BILD further advises that commissioning agencies should ask the following questions of potential training providers:

- How does the training cover the topics listed above?
- What other same-sector service providers has the provider trained? Can I contact them? Can I sit in on some training?
- Will the trainer tailor-make a course to meet the specific needs of staff and service users, or is he/she offering an off-the-peg package?
- Does the trainer have appropriate first aid qualifications and insurance cover?
- Does the course focus on preventive approaches to behaviour management? Or is the emphasis on intervention techniques which the trainer claims staff will use frequently, rather than as a last resort?
- Is follow-up and refresher training included?
- Is the trainer taking a whole-organisation view of the service setting and the role of physical interventions within it?
- Is the trainer willing to visit on site?
- Is the trainer specifically experienced in training on children's issues?

Recording and monitoring

Should physical intervention become necessary, the incident needs to be recorded. Schemes need to ensure mechanisms are in place for this in all aspects of service. Recording should provide a full record of the incident including:

- why problematic behaviour may have occurred
- physical intervention or not
- which holds used
- how long
- any injuries
- considerations of effectiveness and any consequences

- child's response to the incident
- how it was resolved.

Carers, staff and children should be fully supported following difficult incidents and plans reviewed accordingly.

Policy guidance: what needs to be in place?

Written agreements and protocols

Services should ensure that they hold detailed information on children who may require physical interventions. This should cover the range of children who may either injure themselves or others on a regular basis. This information should be shared with management and a strategy agreed. Support and guidance on the management of the risks involved should be sought from specialist staff, who may be from CAMHS (Child and Adolescent Mental Health Services), psychology or psychiatry, and who will need to be staff who see the children in other settings, eg school. Agreements need to be made which cover not only support for individual children, their carers and sitters, but also the resolution of difficult or crisis incidents.

Detailed information on the child

Services should ensure that they have full and detailed information on the child. It is essential in the management of behaviour that information is collated from all settings so that consistency can be ensured. Information should also include a full medical history and information on triggers for difficulties and how they are currently managed.

Drawing up a behaviour management plan

Services should ensure that each child who needs one has a behaviour management plan. The plan should clearly identify the child's behavioural challenges and identify what triggers them. It is important to

The dignity of risk

remember that for most children difficult behaviour is a reaction to fear and insecurity rather than to naughtiness. Identifying fear factors for a child is key to lowering the risk of behavioural difficulties. The behaviour management plan should record current management techniques in all settings and identify any differences. The provider can then draw up a clear agreement on how behaviour will be managed and by whom while the child is in the service.

Establishing a communication picture

Many children requiring behaviour management plans will be children with communication difficulties. Behaviour is a way of communicating when others don't understand us, so it is particularly important that children have a clear communication picture. This should describe how children use gestures, signs and body language to communicate. As a baseline, it should include how happiness and distress are indicated. Examples of these are included in Chapter 6.

Written consent

Parents should be fully involved in the process of drawing up both behaviour management plans and communication pictures. It is also essential that they understand what the scheme can do to manage behaviour and what it cannot do. Some sanctions may be appropriate for parents to use but could not be adopted by the service. Parents and schemes should reach full, signed agreement on techniques and interventions to be used. It would be good practice for parents to have behaviour management training themselves so that their fears and concerns could be discussed.

Training

All those involved with managing difficult behaviour should be trained. No member of staff, carer or volunteer should be assigned to work with a child who needs physical intervention until they have received accredited training. Training should always be provided by an accredited trainer and cannot be cascaded. It is important that accredited trainers have experience in the specific behavioural management needs of children and this should be checked before they are engaged. Records of training received by carers/staff should be kept by service providers so that they are easily available for inspection purposes, and certificates of attendance should be issued. Opportunities to refresh and update the training must be regularly provided. The suggested minimum requirement for updates is two years.

Introductions

The introductory period into service should be used to ensure that child-specific information is fully understood. Carers/staff should ensure they are confident with the information and know how to respond should difficulties arise. They should be assured of support mechanisms and be given clear opportunities to talk through any worries or concerns. Visiting the child in other settings may be a useful part of the process.

Recording incidents

Providers working with children and young people with behavioural management needs should have clear and accessible review and monitoring procedures. This should include ensuring that all staff and carers are able to record incidents where a child potentially or actually injured themselves or others.

Children's risk assessments and behaviour management plans should be reviewed every six months, or sooner if major changes occur. Schemes should also keep a record of all training received by carers, staff and volunteers to ensure that appropriate updates are offered. Services should also record when a child's needs cannot be met because of their behavioural difficulties so that this can contribute to service planning.

Conclusion

Services are yet to develop risk management protocols for challenging behaviour and the introduction of the joint DfES/DH guidance may seem overwhelming. It is important that services realise that these children wait longest and are often being referred from stressful family situations. But the need to place these children and relieve family difficulties should not override the need to prepare and support carers and staff appropriately.

Children who challenge do not benefit from experiencing repeated placement breakdown. The experience of services where carers and staff have been trained show that being confident about managing behaviour makes it much easier to contain and it also changes our approach. Children who challenge are often frightened and insecure. When adults deal with their own insecurities through training they are able to see children or young people as who they are rather than as the behaviour they manifest.

References

DfES and DH (2002) *Joint Guidance on the Use of Restrictive Physical Interventions for Staff Working with Children and Adults who display Extreme Behaviour in Association with Learning and/or Autistic Spectrum Disorders*

British Institute for Learning Disabilities (BILD) (2001) *Code of Practice for Trainers in the Use of Physical Interventions*, available at: www.bild.org.uk

John Harris et al (1996) *Physical Interventions: A policy framework*, BILD

Department for Education and Skills/Department of Health (1996) *Supporting Pupils with Medical Needs: A good practice guide*

Checklist of key points: restrictive physical interventions

1 Draw up **written agreements and protocols**.

2 Obtain detailed **written information on children and young people**.

3 Draw up a **behaviour management plan**.

4 Ensure that the child or young person's **methods of communication** are understood and recorded.

5 Obtain **written consent** from parents to the behaviour management plan and the child or young person's communication picture.

6 Provide **accredited training** to all staff and carers who will be involved in managing behaviour.

7 Allow adequate **time for introductory processes**.

8 Ensure that there is **consistency** in the management of the child or young person's behaviour.

9 Ensure systems are in place for staff and carers to **record incidents**.

10 **Review, monitor and record** behaviour management through clear and accessible review and monitoring procedures.

Appendix   Policy guidance in detail

BILD Code of Practice for Trainers in the Use of Physical Interventions (BILD 2001)

This code of practice aims to be a point of reference and guidance on current best practice for physical interventions training and the selection of trainers. It is intended for use within the policy framework and current legislation.

Good training is seen as appropriate to a specific setting and offers explicit standards, evaluation criteria and procedures. The code covers:
- best interest criteria
- discussion on the principles and attitudes to intervention
- training in the need to avoid interventions and to train only for appropriate techniques for intervention
- health and safety
- course organisation
- monitoring and evaluation, professional conduct and the need for refresher courses.

BILD Physical Interventions Accreditation Scheme

This aims to build a database which will aid in the selection of appropriate organisations delivering training to services caring for people with learning disabilities and/or emotional and behavioural difficulties. The process for accreditation requires the trainer to adopt the BILD Code of Practice (see above), express interest in the accreditation, attend an induction workshop, formally apply to make a submission to a panel, collate a written submission and present this to an accreditation manager, receive a pre-panel assessment visit, and attend a panel, give an oral presentation, and answer any questions arising.

There are trainers who have adopted the code of practice but do not appear on the BILD database, as they have not completed the process of accreditation.

Other relevant guidance: government and professional organisations

Children Act 1989 covers both prohibited and permitted disciplinary measures linking care and control to positive relationships between adults and children. 'Physical restraint should only be used rarely and only to prevent a child harming himself or others or from damaging property. Force should not be used for any other purpose.' Corporal punishment prohibited, nor should physical intervention be used to secure compliance with staff instructions.

1993 Guidance on Permissible Forms of Control in Children's Residential Care restated the situations in which safe restraint and minimum force could be used. Introduced the ideas of pre-emptive steps, dialogue and diversion.

Taking care, Taking control (1996 **Department of Health**) includes a checklist for behaviour management with suggestions for written reporting and debriefing for all physical interventions; emphasises prevention, dignity and safety within a caring ethos.

Care and control of children and young people in foster homes (NFCA 1996) suggests that carers should intervene positively, as might 'reasonable' parents, using the safe and approved methods of the 1993 guidance so that 'young people do not experience variations in discipline'.

1997 The Control of Children in the Public Care: Interpretation of the Children Act 1989 was written to extend the provisions of the Children Act 1989 to all settings and shift the focus from avoiding the risks of action to avoiding the risks and consequence of inaction. 'Children must be listened to and their wishes and feelings taken into consideration. But this does not mean that local authorities, social workers or carers are constrained to abide by the wishes of the child. The wishes of the child can, and indeed should, be overridden in decisions that affect them if this is necessary to safeguard and promote their welfare and protect others.' (p3)

1998 DfEE Circular 10/98 *Section 550A of the Education Act 1996: The Use of Force to Control or Restrain Pupils* states that force must be proportionate and reasonable, the 'minimum needed to achieve the desired result', and in the form of permissible interventions. Though the focus is on de-escalating techniques some measures could be taken 'in the most exceptional circumstances where there is no alternative'. The circular was criticised for allowing too much discretion for teachers. There is strong opinion that it contravenes the 1989 UN Convention on the Rights of the Child.

2000 Care Standards Act built upon the preceding legislation and good practice. It offered a prescription for policy, procedures and guidance.

2002 DfES: *Autistic Spectrum Disorder: Good Practice Guidance* sets out the principles underlying effective provision and offers a set of pointers for good practice. Leads directly to the 2002 joint DfES/Department of Health guidance.

Sample forms and guidance

It was clear in developing this handbook that the area of managing behaviour is the most underdeveloped one for services. There is little in place currently within the sector and much of the following is material borrowed from residential services. It has been included because much of it is transferable and adaptable.

The following is a list of forms included in this chapter, and what they are used for. The forms were supplied by different organisations and local authorities, and have been adapted for publication in this handbook. They are intended to be examples of good practice and can be copied or adapted for use by other organisations. Copies of originals can be obtained from Shared Care Network.

Form 1 This policy on physical interventions provides a detailed policy statement on the management of physical interventions within a school setting. Much of the headings and information are transferable to community settings. Chelfham Mill School

Form 2 This behavioural development plan provides a useful outline for a behaviour management plan. Sunfield School

Form 3 Critical incident support plan. This form looks at managing and investigating behaviour and provides useful sections on consent and responsibilities.

Form 4 Children's Trust checklist of behaviours for risk assessment.

Form 5 This form is used for recording a difficult incident, managing an adult response to it and analysing an incident.

As formats become available which apply specifically to community services they will be available from Shared Care Network.

Form 1

Chelfham Mill School

This provides a detailed policy statement on the management of physical interventions within a school setting. Much of the headings and information are transferable to community settings.

Aims

- to establish a code of conduct which sets out the control and restraint measures permitted within the school
- to ensure physical intervention is only used in the best interests of the pupils with due regard for their well-being
- to ensure the regular monitoring review and evaluation of physical interventions used within the school.

Objectives

- to provide thorough and comprehensive training to all relevant staff in handling and avoiding aggression
- to provide thorough and comprehensive training to all relevant staff in the permitted forms of non-restrictive and restrictive physical intervention
- to provide regular refresher training to all relevant staff
- to involve pupils in the creation of their own positive handling plan
- to have up-to-date and regularly reviewed individual behaviour profiles, including a risk assessment related to possible violence and aggression
- to have a thorough and effective system of recording and reporting non-restrictive and restrictive physical interventions
- to have a thorough and effective system for monitoring
- to review and evaluate the use of physical intervention.

The law

The use of physical intervention within the school will operate within the law, ensuring that:
- any physical intervention should be consistent with the legal obligations and responsibilities of the school and its staff and the rights and protection afforded to people with learning disabilities under the law
- it is responsible for the provision of care, including physical interventions, which are in the pupils best interests.

Values

The school upholds the value base defined by BILD/NAS in its use of physical interventions through this policy.
- Physical interventions should only be used in the best interests of the pupils.
- Pupils should be treated fairly and with courtesy and respect.
- Pupils should be helped to make choices and be involved in decisions which affect their lives.
- There should be experiences and opportunities for learning which are appropriate to the pupils' interests and abilities.

Prevention of challenging behaviour

The school will ensure through training and individual review that the prevention of challenging behaviour is addressed in the following ways:
- careful management of setting conditions, both personal and environmental (primary prevention)
- the development of secondary prevention using non-physical interventions to deal with episodes before pupils become violent
- individual strategies, including directions for using physical interventions, for each pupil presenting challenging behaviour.

Promoting the best interests of pupils

The best interests of pupils will be promoted through:
- the use of individual behaviour profiles to establish individualised procedures for pupils presenting challenging behaviours, thus enabling staff to respond effectively ensuring the safety of all concerned
- the use of other strategies designed to help pupils learn alternative, non-challenging behaviour
- the planning of physical intervention – justified by knowledge of the client, previous interventions, evaluation of risk and the advice of an expert body
- regularly reviewing the use of physical interventions.

Physical intervention and risk assessment

Through the pupils' individual behaviour profiles the potential hazards of using physical interventions has been subject to a risk assessment.

Minimising risk and promoting the well-being of pupils

In order to minimise risk to pupils through the use of physical intervention, the following principles are in place:
- physical interventions should be employed using the minimum reasonable force
- any single physical intervention should be employed for the minimum duration of time
- for individual pupils, interventions should be sanctioned for the shortest possible time, consistent with their best interests
- physical interventions should not cause pain
- physical interventions should be approved after individual assessments to identify contraindications
- pupils who regularly receive physical interventions should be routinely assessed for signs of injury or psychological distress.

Responsibilities

Senior management are responsible for:
- developing and implementing policies on the use of physical interventions
- providing written evidence on procedures for staff
- ensuring a system is in place for incidents that involve physical intervention to be recorded clearly, comprehensively and promptly
- ensuring all pupils and interested others have ready access to a formal complaints procedure
- the safety and well-being of staff
- encouraging staff to monitor all physical interventions and report incidents giving cause for concern
- ensuring staff deployment is organised so that appropriately trained staff are available to respond to incidents requiring physical intervention.

Staff training

Staff training is fundamental to the implementation of this policy and the school will ensure that:
- all staff required to use physical interventions will receive training on knowledge, skills and values
- training will be provided by an instructor with relevant experience and accredited by BILD
- staff should employ only those physical interventions which they have been trained to use.

Monitoring, review and evaluation

The use of physical interventions and the effectiveness of this policy and training will be monitored on a regular basis as part of the whole school monitoring system.
- Incidents involving the use of physical interventions are monitored daily.
- The use of physical interventions is monitored half-termly.
- Physical intervention training is updated annually, at a minimum.
- Individual behaviour profiles are monitored termly and updated at least annually, in line with the annual education review and in consultation with the pupils.
- The policy will be reviewed annually.

Actions required are identified through monitoring and plans put into place to address them. This information will be used when reviewing the policy.

This policy must only be used in conjunction with a full training package and supporting documentation.

Physical interventions for challenging behaviour/managing behaviour

Form 2

Sunfield School

Name _____ Date _____

One month review _____ Termly review dates _____

Description of behaviour _____

_____

Possible triggers _____

Possible function(s) _____

Risk assessment
Evaluate risk posed by this behaviour to child, others, environment, etc. _____

_____

Behaviour objective (long-term goal) _____

Proactive strategies
Step-by-step strategy including environmental aspects (noise, people, activity) and communication aids.

1 _____

2 _____

3 _____

4 _____

5 _____

6 _____

Reinforcements

1 _____

2 _____

3 _____

4 _____

Reactive strategies
Again step-by-step, including calming, verbal/non-verbal interaction, re-direction.

1 _____

2 _____

3 _____

4 _____

5 _____

6 _____

Agreed by
House _____ School _____

Parents _____ Other _____

Form 3

For _____ Drawn up on _____

Plan background

The specific behaviour of concern is _____
_____
_____

Those involved in drawing up the plan are _____
_____
_____

Those who have seen the plan and agree with it are _____
_____
_____

The things that are being done to find out why the behaviour occurs are _____
_____
_____

Plan details

The things that we will do to prevent incidents

1 Changes in environment, activities, routines, support _____
_____
_____

2 Management of known triggers _____
_____
_____

3 Ways of working when there is a conflict _____
_____
_____

4 Ways of working to reduce identified increased in arousal _____
_____
_____

5 The things that we will do to reduce the impact of incidents _____
_____
_____

The ways that we will respond to incidents

What the individual does   *What we will do*

First signs   _____   _____
              _____   _____
              _____   _____

Build-up   _____   _____
              _____   _____
              _____   _____

Final level   _____   _____
              _____   _____
              _____   _____

The ways that we will manage the aftermath of the incident

1 How we will work with the individual _____
_____
_____

2 How we will work with the others affected by the incident _____
_____
_____

The way that we will evaluate the plan's effectiveness

Review system details _____
_____
_____

Form 4

The Children's Trust

Child's name _____ Date of birth _____

House _____

Name of assessor (print) _____

Job role _____

Date of previous assessment _____ Date of this assessment _____

Risks to assess	Immediate risk identified (yes/no, if yes specify)	Factors/triggers
1 Risk of deliberate harm to self (eg self-injury, cutting, overdose)		
2 Risk of accidental harm to self (eg wandering out of house or no awareness of road safety. Medical problems causing poor swallow reflex, epilepsy, diabetic coma, lack of insight, thought processing problems, lack of spatial awareness)		
3 Risk of physical abuse to others (eg physical aggression to staff, family, visitors, peers or other children which may cause injuries)		
4 Risk of verbal abuse to others (eg sexually or emotionally abusive or offensive language)		
5 Risk of sexual abuse to others (eg touches staff, family, visitors, peers or other children inappropriately)		
6 Risk of self-neglect (eg neglects physical appearance or personal hygiene, refuses food and/ or drinks)		
7 Risk of damage to property or the environment (eg breaks furniture, equipment, arson or fire setting)		

For any of the risks identified above please complete the table below:

Risk number	Prevention methods	Graduated response which seeks to minimise conflict and avoid confrontation	Planned strategies	Likelihood of adverse outcomes	Identified contra-indications to a physical intervention

Signatures   Date   Signature   Print name

Assessor _____

Key worker (if not assessor) _____

Head of house _____

Copy sent to   Date   Signature   Print name

Nurse manager to file in child's records _____

Clinical psychologist _____

Registered manager _____

The dignity of risk

Form 5

Recording and analysis of a behaviour incident

a Need to identify the function of the behaviour.
- What is the person trying to communicate
- From the individual's perspective, what is being gained from the behaviour.
- From the individual's view, what is being escaped or avoided by the behaviour.

b What causes the behaviour to be challenging?
- What is the impact of the behaviour on:
  i the individual
  ii those around them.

c What causes, or what is the motivation for, the behaviour?

d Identify effective strategies for dealing with the behaviour.

In order to establish the above factors, a behaviour incident needs to be broken down, recorded and analysed into the following categories:

1 Precursors and antecedents
2 Behaviour
3 Staff response
4 Consequences.

Causes and function of behaviour

Precursors

What did the child communicate prior to the behaviour:
- did they make any requests?
- did they make any statements about how they felt?

What were the actions of the child prior to the behaviour incident:
- were there any noticeable changes in behaviour or mood, eg fidgeting and pacing?
- excitability
- quiet and withdrawn
- tired.

Were there any noticeable physical factors, eg:
- flushed face
- hyperventilation
- pallor.

Antecedents

Events and influencing factors preceding a behaviour.

Physical factors
- Diet – certain foods may contain colourants and additives which can cause hyperactivity and allergic reactions in some children and exacerbate behaviour.
- Sufficient fluid intake will prevent dehydration which can lead to confusion and disorientation, as can constipation.

Physical disabilities
- A child with a physical disability may find it difficult to complete certain tasks due to lack of co-ordination and dexterity. This could cause frustration and anger.
- Equipment such as wheelchairs and spinal jackets may cause discomfort, and for children who are unable to express this, they may use other forms of communication which may be construed as challenging behaviour.

Physical interventions for challenging behaviour/managing behaviour

Incident analysis sheet

Name of pupil _____ Date of report _____

Name of person reporting _____ Position _____

Type of incident (please tick)

Injury to other pupil ☐ Injury to self ☐ Injury to staff ☐

Physical containment ☐ Property damage ☐ Absconding/leaving session ☐

Non-performance ☐ Verbal aggression ☐

Description of incident

Date of incident _____ Time incident started _____ Time incident ended _____

Where was the pupil when the behaviour occurred? _____

Who was working with the pupil when the behaviour occurred? _____

Where were the staff at the time of the incident? _____

Who was next to the pupil at the time of the incident? _____

Who else (staff or pupils) were in the immediate area when the incident occurred? _____

_____

Describe the general atmosphere (ie noise level, others having tantrums, staff attitude) _____

_____

_____

What was the pupil doing at the time of the incident? Describe the activity, task, event or interaction.

_____

_____

What occurred immediately before the incident? Describe demands, changes in activity, interactions, etc.

_____

_____

Describe what the pupil did during the incident (eg hit with fist, kicked with foot, etc). _____

_____

_____

Describe the severity of the incident (eg damage, injuries, etc). _____

_____

_____

Consequences _____

_____

_____

The dignity of risk

6 Towards child-centred risk management

This chapter covers
Communication and communication passports
Final thoughts in relation to managing risk
Examples of communication passports

Much of this handbook has, inevitably, been concerned with forms and formats, insurance and liability. It is easy with risk to become lost in bureaucracy, to believe that the forms are an end in themselves rather than a tool.

It is important throughout the process to remember the child at the centre of it. The example forms in the handbook have been chosen partly because they reflect a move towards child-centred assessments. Old formats, particularly for moving and handling, are still very medical and use language which can be dehumanising and offensive.

The move towards child-centred risk assessment, however, is still in its very early stages. Some organisations like Triangle (www.triangle-services.co.uk) and the CALL Centre (www.callcentrescotland.org.uk) in Edinburgh have pioneered new approaches which bring together various elements of a child's life in a child-friendly document. These approaches have been responses to the challenges faced by children who have a whole range of needs and therefore several different plans. For example, a child with very complex needs could have a child information form, an invasive care plan, a moving and handling plan and a behaviour management plan. The task is to bring these together to ensure information is shared and the whole child is represented.

Communication and communication passports

The issue of communication is central to the management of risk. Many children are non-verbal and non-signing, but they all communicate – in an individual way. Understanding this individual communication helps everyone relate to the child and read early signals of happiness and distress. Services in a number of fields are developing exciting methods of understanding communication and developing communication plans and pictures. Form 1 from Essex shows how this can be done in a simple way.

Communication passports

Another way of working on communication is the development of communication passports. These are written records, videos or object-based records of how a person communicates and some of the things they like to communicate about. These help everyone involved in the life of the child to have the same information and follow the same planning. Communication passports tell you how to give information to a person so that they can understand it. This may mean altering the way you communicate, by using signs or symbols, for example.

Communication passports will also tell you how a person communicates and how to interpret that communication. They explain communication that might be subtle and open to interpretation. Many passports will also hold information about important people, events and activities in a person's life.

Communication passports are creative and individual. While extensive passports can be complex and time-consuming to complete, the formats give us ideas for how to begin to change our recording and formats. It would be helpful for services to find out whether communication passports are being developed in their area.

At the end of this chapter are some examples of the type and style of information held in communication passports (Forms 2 to 7) from CALL Centre, University of Edinburgh.

Final thoughts in relation to managing risk

The management of risk will remain an inherent part of the way we provide services for disabled children and their families. There are no current predictions about a changing direction for the disability population; if anything, the needs of disabled children are likely to become more complex.

Managing risk can seem difficult for schemes, and individual workers and families may occasionally wonder if it's worth it. As a reminder, it's worth it for the following reasons.

- It is the dignity of risk that allows disabled people to live their lives. Taking no risks means returning disabled children to the institutions, where, despite a no-risk approach, inhuman practices and abuse were rife.
- It is the job of services to manage risk. Risk cannot be removed completely, just assessed and managed.
- As advocates of the rights of disabled children and their families, service providers should encourage them to have the opportunities and experiences that all children and families do.
- It is still possible to place children with significant risk management issues in family support services. The management of risk, however, requires an ongoing process.

- Promoting risk management does enable services to say no if necessary. It may be that for some children alternative services are more appropriate. Such a decision must, however, be made following an assessment. Leaving children and young people on waiting lists or records of unmet need, when it is known that the likelihood of placement is minimal, constitutes poor practice and should be recognised as such.
- Alongside the duty to promote the use of services by disabled children, we have a duty to safeguard the health and safety of carers, sitters and staff. The two duties should be compatible and both are necessary for a competent risk management policy.

In practice, as a starting point services must:
- Ensure that all children who need one have a risk assessment. Services should have a clear policy on who carries out risk assessments and on support available.
- Services should carry out an audit of current risk areas – including invasive care procedures, moving and handling and challenging behaviour. Services cannot manage risk appropriately if they do not understand the risks they are carrying. Audit results should be discussed with senior management, who should make a decision on how these risks will be managed and ensure that all parties involved sign an agreement.
- All service providers must have training in risk management areas by an accredited trainer. The use of cascade training does not fulfil this requirement. Training must be updated at regular intervals – a minimum of every two years.
- Issues about equipment are difficult and should be referred to senior managers. If equipment is not available, this should be recorded as an unmet need.

The dignity of risk

Examples of communication passports

The following are two sets of forms which illustrate communication passports.

Form 1 This is a holistic assessment for a child with complex needs designed by Essex. Within it is contained a useful communication guide.

Forms 2 to 8 The example papers here are taken from the communication passports of various children and adults. They reproduce passport papers taken from: S Millar (1997/2002) *Personal Communication Passports Information Pack*, available from CALL Centre, University of Edinburgh, Holyrood Road, Edinburgh EH8 8AG, tel 0131 651 6236.

For further information see S Millar and S Aitken (2003) *Personal Communication Passports: Guidelines for good practice*, published by the CALL Centre, ISBN 1 898042 217.

Form 1

Essex

Example of a unified plan for 'Fred'

Example of Fred's pen portrait, prepared by Fred and his carers and teacher (this pen portrait could be written in the third person).

I am 8 years old.

I am usually happy and contented and able to show adults who know me when I am uncomfortable, sad or in pain. I love people talking to me and I can recognise familiar voices. My movements can be a bit uncontrolled. I only have very limited vision so I rely on my hearing and my ability to touch to make sense of where I am and what I should be doing. I need help to be able to move from one position to another and will try and help in movement activity. Sometimes I get uncomfortable so moving me and helping me change my posture including my sitting or standing position makes me feel better. I will smile if I'm OK.

I enjoy being cuddled and reach out to touch faces and hair. I like to try and find objects that are within my reach and I can anticipate a simple, noisy cause and effect activity. I love being free to wriggle around on the mat and I stop moving when I hear a sound or feel a touch. I enjoy standing in my supportive standing frame and I can take some weight through my feet when closely supported by someone who knows me well. When I sit in my supportive seating chair I am able to hold my head up better and also reach for something and use both my hands. I can get quite tired very quickly and then I need extra help to hold my head up or I need a rest.

Due to my very sensitive mouth, I have difficulty eating and drinking and have a 'tummy peg' to make sure I have enough food and drink. I have severe epileptic fits. My health care plans support both these medical needs. I am totally dependent on adults for my personal care.

Example of the goals and aspirations illustrating the person-centred approach to planning

1 Fred to be able to make himself understood to unfamiliar adults so that he can broaden his circle of support and his carers can be more confident about other people looking after and caring for him.
2 Fred to be able to make some choices in what he would like to do so that he learns how to make decisions.
3 Fred to be able to stand, with adult support, so he can help with his mobility.
4 Fred to be able to take an active role in his personal and self-help skills.
5 Fred to be able to activate a wide variety of cause and effect toys so that he expands his opportunities for play.
6 Fred's carers wish to be able to look after Fred at home for as long as possible.

Goals	What is happening now	People involved in helping Fred and his carers	Actions	Monitor and review – including timescales and dates and the opportunity for all involved to contribute
1 Fred to be able to make himself understood to unfamiliar adults.	Fred is able to make himself understood by adults who know him very well.	Carers, teachers, key worker, speech and language therapist (SaLT), occupational therapist (OT), short break and shared carers, family support workers, sessional workers at the local activity clubs	Joint re-assessment by SaLT, teacher and carers.	SaLT, teacher and key worker every term. Frequent recording.
2 Fred to be able to make choices.	Fred is able to make a few choices by demonstrating, to familiar adults, whether he likes or dislikes an activity.	Carers, teachers, key worker, OT, SaLT, short break and shared carers, family support workers, sessional workers at local activity clubs	Joint re-assessment by SaLT, OT, teacher and carer.	Teacher, SaLT, key worker every term. Frequent recording.
3 Fred to be able to stand, with adult support.	Fred is able to stand momentarily, with maximum adult support.	Carers, PT, teacher, key workers, family support workers, short break workers, shared carers	Re-assessment and teaching for selected staff and carers by PT.	Teacher, PT and OT. Episode of direct intervention every half-term PT. Orthotics every term (PT).
4 Fred to be able to take an active role in his personal care and self-help skills.	Fred is sensitive to having a spoon or toothbrush in his mouth and requires maximum support for all personal care including eating and drinking activities. He is 'tummy peg' fed.	Carers, teachers, specialist nurses, dietician, SaLT, OT, dental hygienist, key worker, short break and shared carers, family support workers	SaLT, OT to review de-sensitising programme	Team around the child, every half-term co-ordinated by school nurse
5 Fred to be able to activate a wide variety of cause and effect toys.	Fred is able to play with two familiar cause and effect toys.	Carers, teachers, key workers, OT, family support workers, short break, shared carers and sessional workers at local activity clubs	Update from OT, positioning for being able to use hands.	Teacher, OT and key worker every term. Frequent recording.
6 Fred's carers to be able to look after him at home for as long as possible.	Carers require support from short break, shared carers and family support workers. Carers have many disturbed nights. Carers not confident about holiday activities.	Social worker, short break and shared carers, family support workers, sessional workers at local activity clubs	Referral to doctor for further advice.	Practical support arrangements reviewed as per LAC regulations. Monitor of sleep patterns every half-term – parent and teacher/ key worker.

Towards child-centred risk management

Fred to be able to make himself understood to unfamiliar adults

Key skills	Component skill	Key objectives or learning targets	Evidence of success	Strategies to support
Personal and social	Personal	To define a positive 'no' response	Demonstrates the positive 'no' response to familiar adults who reinforce the response	Communication passport
	Social	To actively participate in group activities with familiar and unfamiliar people	Consistently holding or lifting up his head and/or smiling/vocalising when called by his name even if he does not recognise the voice	Posture and movement
Communication	Speaking	To be able to demonstrate a definite 'no' which is accurately interpreted by an unfamiliar adult	Unfamiliar adults, such as a different family support worker is able to accurately interpret a negative response from Fred	Communication passport
Etc.				

Fred to be able to make choices

Key skills	Component skill	Key objectives or learning targets	Evidence of success	Strategies to support
Communication	Speaking	To begin to communicate choices by eye pointing and smiling/making happy vocalisations sounds.	Smiles and keeps smiling when eye pointing to a chosen activity/toy which he can then participate in/play with.	Communication passport
	Listening	To begin to respond to some key words within the context of very familiar routines.	Smiles and vocalises to the names of familiar people.	
Mathematics	Measures and shapes	To explore different objects placed within his reach.	Moving his hands to touch and knock wobbly sounding toys.	Posture and movement
	Making sense of problems	To feel a range of substances and materials and begin to discriminate between them.	Keeping his hands on soft gentle materials whilst moving his hands away from harsh materials.	Posture and movement
Problem solving		To anticipate certain actions and effects.	Shows excitement when waiting for a toy to make a noise or move.	
Physical	Manipulation	To purposefully feel and touch objects.	Reaching out and exploring objects.	Posture and movement

Fred to be able to stand with adult support

Key skills	Component skill	Key objectives or learning targets	Evidence of success	Strategies to support
Physical	Movement	To be able to take some weight through his legs when supported by a familiar adult.	Taking weight through his legs when transferring from his wheelchair to a chair	Daily stands in the supportive standing frame. Assisted supported standing. Posture and movement. Moving and therapeutic handling.

Key skills	Component skill	Key objectives or learning targets	Evidence of success	Strategies to support
		To be able to bridge	Bridging whilst lying on the mat	Posture and movement. PE schemes of work.
		To be able to freely kick his legs	Kicking a large light ball with R and L feet whilst lying on the mat or sitting with support	PE schemes of work
Etc.				

Fred to be able to take an active role in his personal care and self help skill

Key skills	Component skill	Key objectives or learning targets	Evidence of success	Strategies to support
Physical	Movement	To be able to assist in personal care by 'bridging'	Actively bridging at each personal care session	Posture and movement
	Manipulation	To be able to hold feeding tube	Holding the tube during lunch and tea time feeds	Healthcare plans
Communication		To be able to indicate when thirsty	Sipping to drink from a shallow spoon after indicating he is thirsty by sticking his tongue out	Feeding and drinking
		To tolerate having his teeth cleaned	Keeping his head still and his mouth relaxed when it is teeth cleaning time	De-sensitising programme
Personal and social	Personal	To be able to recognise 'object of reference'	Routinely holding the appropriate object of reference	Posture and movement. Communication passport
		To assist with removing coat	Holding sleeve of coat to help pull it off	Posture and movement

Fred to be able to activate a wide variety of cause and effect toys

Key skills	Component skill	Key objectives or learning targets	Evidence of success	Strategies to support
ICT	Modelling and control	To be able to operate a variety of touch switch toys	Lifting hands and placing on switch and smiling at the effect with familiar toys, and lifting and placing hands on the same switch but activating a different toy and developing an awareness of the difference	Posture and movement Communication
Study skills	Concentration	To become less reliant on adult support when playing with switch toys	Switching cause and effect toys off and on, smiling at the effect and repeating action independent of adults	
Physical	Manipulation	To be able to relax his hands and place them on a switch	Placing his hands purposefully onto a switch with minimal adult prompt	Posture and movement. Communication
Etc.				

Towards child-centred risk management

Fred's carers to be able to look after him at home for as long as possible

Key objectives or learning targets	Evidence of success	Strategies to support
Fred's carers to consistently have undisturbed nights	Fred sleeps through the night	School timetable to support regular rest periods, activities after lunch and morning hydro sessions to encourage Fred to stay awake all day. Taxi to have a supply of Fred's favourite music tapes. Structured bedtime routine and healthcare plans in place. Fred to have sleep system (posture support).
Fred's carers to receive short breaks	Fred's practical support arrangements are in place and reviewed regularly	Practical support arrangements: • 20 nights of short break arrangements • 7.30 until 8.30 family support three days a week, term time • One Saturday in a month shared care
Fred's carers to feel confident about Fred attending the local activity group	Fred is able to communicate simple needs through his communication passport	Communication passport. Posture and movement/moving and therapeutic handling. Healthcare plans

Example of a quick reference guide

Prepared by parents/carers, teacher/plan operator and the team around the child
(ensure there are links to the goals and skills to be learned).

Encourage	Discourage
Sitting on the mat with my legs crossed with support from an adult. Sitting straight in my chair. Holding my head up and playing with activities with my hands. Making me choose what toys I want to play with.	Slumping against support from an adult with both my legs twisted. Twisting my head in my chair. Putting my head on my hands and biting my knuckles. Just giving me the same toys to play with.

The dignity of risk

Example of a communication guide

Prepared by parents/carers, teacher/plan operator and the 'team around the child'.

When I do this	People think I mean	You should do
Smile	I am saying 'yes'. I am happy. I like what I am doing.	Give me time to smile and act according to my answer of 'yes'.
Lift up my left hand and bang the tray (I am just learning to do this)	I am trying to say 'no'.	Ask me the question again and act according to my answer of 'no'.
Close my eyes and moan	I am uncomfortable. I am sad. I am bored. I don't like what I am doing.	1 Ask me if I am uncomfortable, if I smile, move my position, for example, if I am in my wheelchair – take me out and let me stretch out on a mat. If I'm on the mat, sit me back into my chair. See my practical support plans to help you do this properly. 2 If I don't smile, just talk to me and see if you can cheer me up. 3 If I don't smile, see if I would like to do something else, offer me a choice.
Keep letting my head fall forwards	I am tired.	Let me rest, stretched out on the mat, or in my side lying board.
Stick my tongue out	I am thirsty.	Give me a little warm drink of water from my special mug. See my practical support plans to help you do this properly.
Cry but there are no tears	I am cross.	Check to see if I need anything, change my activity or include me in an activity. Move me from sitting next to someone who may upsetting me.
Screw up my hands	I feel very unsafe.	Give me more support and help.
Screw my nose up and twist my head	I have got a tummy ache.	Help me change my position. Give me sips of warm water to drink.

Food for thought

We have *big* arguments about the best way for me to eat and drink.

Mum says I should be fed like I was at home. She says it's slow and messy if I try to feed myself and she's worried that I won't get enough to eat and that I'll waste away and get ill.

My keyworkers say that now I'm grown up I should be learning to feed myself and that it's childish for me to be fed. They say it's insulting for me to wear a bib like a baby.

And I reckon that *I'm* the most important person in all this.

I hate getting my clothes dirty, I'd much rather cover them up. But it doesn't have to be a baby bib – a big sports towel does the job fine, or an old shirt slipped on back to front over my top.

I hate it when I feel hungry or tired, and my food gets cold. I'd rather be fed, to get a good hot meal.

I do like to practise eating by myself, but not all the time. And I'd rather do it mostly with snacks and sandwiches and cold foods, and not when I'm out and people are watching.

I'm pretty good at drinking by myself with my own cup. I just need reminding to have plenty of drinks so I don't dry up.

The dignity of risk

Some helpful hints

- Please don't ask me more than one thing at a time, for example, 'Is your sister in the North School or is she in the South School?'.

  If I look up AND down to answer these questions, you'll be confused!

- Please don't make things too complicated, for example, 'Are you going horse-riding this week? Someone said it might be cancelled. Is it finished for the term? Or is it next week that it's cancelled?'

  I'll just burst out laughing if you try all that at once! Sorry!

- If you want me to choose something – which music I like or the answer to a question – try this:

  'Rachel, which group do you like? Look up for Take That, look down for Oasis, or look at me for Blur.'

I can hear you!

Bend the knees

My hearing is not 100%, but I can usually hear if you speak in front of me, at the height of my face. Hold my face in your hand and speak into my face so I can 'feel' you speaking to me.

Call my name

Always say 'Simon' to me before you start to speak, so that I know to pay attention.

Keep it simple

Just say short sentences to me, and stress the key word. Like, 'Simon, DINNER time now'.

Wired for sound

I love music. I can hear it better if you put the Walkman head-phones on me – if it's just playing in the room it just sounds like a big buzz. My favourite tape is the 'Singing kettle'.

Touch me!

It helps me to pay attention if you touch me and hold me while you are talking.

Hear my voice

I hope I'll be able to talk a bit, one day. My practice position for making sounds is lying face down over your knees, while you jiggle your knees up and down or else vibrate the outside edge of your hands on my back.

The dignity of risk

When I'm unsettled

I often become unsettled. It happens when I become frustrated, usually because people don't understand me or if there is something I really want to do but I can't.

People don't like what I do when I'm unsettled.

I tend to scream and shout. I sometimes cry, bite or push. I stamp from foot to foot very quickly and I often shake my head from side to side. Sometimes I sit or lie down on the floor.

I'm working on this at nursery with Alice and Mrs Jones, and at home with Mum.

This is how they try to help me.
- They try to stay calm.
- They talk to me in a quiet way.
- They sometimes ask me questions to find out what is wrong.
- They sometimes take me into a quiet area and stay with me until I settle down. (Sometimes I can be unsettled for a few seconds and at other times it can be a bit longer.)

What I need

Three things in particular make a big difference to how I behave generally — and to how I communicate. If you bear these in mind, we should get along fine together.

1 My health, and the drugs I'm taking
   Sometimes I just don't feel at all well, and I just sleep most of the time. It's no good trying to make me 'perk up'. Just leave me alone, please. (But keep an eye on me.)

2 The way other people relate to me
   I'm used to positive encouragement, and that's what like. I appreciate simple explanations. I do not — repeat not — respond well to pressure (especially being physically made to do something) or to threats!

3 I need plenty of time
   It takes me a while to take things in, when you speak to me, before I react — there's a sort of 'delay' while I process things. Wait a bit — I promise you it's worth it!

The dignity of risk

Eating and drinking

Please DO!

- Sit opposite me and chat to me when you're helping me eat. I can't really see you, but I can hear you better, and it helps me keep my head straight and in the right position.
- Give me food that's fairly dry and firm (mashed potato consistency) so I have something to get my teeth into.
- Put the spoon under my side teeth, on a different side of my mouth on each alternate spoonful, so that I get practice trying to chew on both sides and don't end up all 'lop-sided'.
- Help me close my lips once the food's in, by putting your thumb gently under the middle of my lower lip, and pushing up, gently. Help me chew by gently rotating your finger on the outside of my cheek, where the food is.
- Give me plenty of time to each and finish my meal. It may not seem like it to you, but I really do like food, and I need all I'm given, otherwise I may lose weight and get ill.

Please DON'T!

- Don't give me runny, mushy food like jelly. If it's soup, I'll drink it from my cup.
- Don't tip my head back and 'pour food down the back of my throat. I might choke, and then you'd be sorry.
- Don't scrape the food off the spoon on my front teeth, and leave me with my mouth open. It'll either fall back and choke me, or fall out the front again.
- If I bite on the spoon, don't try to wrench it out from between my teeth – that makes me grip harder. Try distracting me (tickling?) and wait until I relax my jaws again, then tweak it out quickly.

Good luck! I really am trying, believe it or not.
(Yes, I know – very trying ...)

Form 8

Managing my behaviour

Triggers

An unexpected change in routine
Or even a change of person
Too many changes at any one time can really throw me
Sometimes I don't want to do what I am being asked to do
Sometimes I don't understand what is expected of me
I can get frustrated when people don't understand me

Early warning

My thumb goes in my mouth and my other hand starts to tug at my hair
I can then start to make a lot of noise
My breathing becomes much deeper
I can also adopt a John Cleese style 'silly walk'!

First step

Explain the situation to me. 'It's different today, Bob. You are doing
shopping at Safeways, you are not eating in the cafe, it is nearly snack
time and then you will be cooking in the kitchen. Repeat this several times
– as often as need be.
Or, ask me 'What is it Bob? You tell me.' Encourage me to show you with
my signs/hands.
Or, you can try guessing 'Is it sore?', 'Are you hungry?' I will say yes (clap
my hands) or no (shake my head) appropriately.
Moan initially, then become more noisy. I could then become angry or
upset and try to scratch you.
When things get too bad I try to take my clothes off.
At times I soil myself, although this has been rare lately.

If that doesn't work I could ... Next

Sometimes I need to be taken out of the situation in order to calm down. I
should always be taken out if I start to scratch, etc. A quiet area away
from other people is best. I should only go back once I have quietened
down. You can move away from me and stand quietly if I am trying to
scratch you.
Make sure I am safe, the other children are safe and you are safe.